Revise GCSE

Additional Science

Ian Hone   yer and Emma Poole

Contents

			This book and your GCSE course	4
			Preparing for the exams	6
			Six ways to improve your grade	7
			How Science Works	8

Biology

1	Genetics	1.1	Genes and chromosomes	9
		1.2	Passing on genes	11
		1.3	Gene technology	13
			Sample GCSE questions	17
			Exam practice questions	18

2	Cells and molecules	2.1	Cells and organisation	19
		2.2	DNA and protein synthesis	22
		2.3	Proteins and enzymes	24
		2.4	Cell division	26
		2.5	Growth and development	29
		2.6	Transport in cells	32
		2.7	Respiration	35
			Sample GCSE questions	38
			Exam practice questions	40

3	Sampling organisms	3.1	Sampling techniques	43
		3.2	Food production – photosynthesis	46
		3.3	Farming techniques	48
			Sample GCSE questions	52
			Exam practice questions	53

4	Physiology	4.1	Transport in animals	56
		4.2	Transport in plants	59
		4.3	Digestion and absorption	61
			Sample GCSE questions	64
			Exam practice questions	66

Chemistry

5	Atoms and materials	5.1	Atomic structure	69
		5.2	Atoms and the periodic table	72
		5.3	Chemical reactions and atoms	75
		5.4	The periodic table	78
		5.5	Balancing equations	81
		5.6	Ionic and covalent bonding	84
		5.7	Ionic and covalent structures	88
		5.8	Group 7	91
		5.9	Nanoparticles	95
		5.10	Synthesis	96
			Sample GCSE questions	100
			Exam practice questions	102

6	Metals, tests and analysis	6.1	Metals	104
		6.2	Group 1	106
		6.3	Transition metals	109
		6.4	Chemical tests 1	111
		6.5	Chemical tests 2	113
		6.6	Analysis	116
			Sample GCSE questions	120
			Exam practice questions	121

7	Salts and solubility	7.1	Making salts	123
		7.2	Metal carbonate reactions	125
		7.3	The electrolysis of sodium chloride	127
		7.4	Water and solubility	129
			Sample GCSE questions	131
			Exam practice questions	132
8	Calculation and physical chemistry	8.1	Relative formula mass and percentage composition	133
		8.2	Calculations	136
		8.3	Rates of reaction	139
		8.4	Reversible reactions and the Haber process	143
		8.5	Exothermic and endothermic reactions	146
		8.6	Explaining energy changes	149
			Sample GCSE questions	152
			Exam practice questions	154

Physics

9	Forces and motion	9.1	Distance, speed and velocity	156
		9.2	Speed, velocity and acceleration	159
		9.3	Forces	162
		9.4	Acceleration and momentum	166
		9.5	Action and reaction	168
		9.6	Work and energy	172
		9.7	Energy and power	175
			Sample GCSE questions	179
			Exam practice questions	181
10	Electricity	10.1	Electrostatic effects	184
		10.2	Uses of electrostatics	186
		10.3	Electric currents	190
		10.4	Voltage or potential difference	192
		10.5	Resistance and resistors	195
		10.6	Special resistors	198
		10.7	The mains supply	201
			Sample GCSE questions	205
			Exam practice questions	207
11	Radioactivity	11.1	Atomic structure	210
		11.2	Radioactive decay	213
		11.3	Living with radioactivity	216
		11.4	Uses of radioactive material	219
		11.5	Nuclear fission and fusion	223
			Sample GCSE questions	227
			Exam practice questions	229
			Answers	232
			Index	238
			Periodic table	240

This book and

Web Address

Specification Number

Exam Assessed Units and Modules

At least 40% of assessment must be carried out at the end of the course.

For students starting the GCSE course from September 2012 onwards, all assessment (100%) must take place at the end of the course.

Controlled Assessment

Covering:
· Research, planning and risk assessment
· Data collection
· Processing, analysis and evaluation

Chapter Map*

AQA		
www.aqa.org.uk		
4408		4409
Three papers All papers: 1 hr 60 marks 25% of GCSE All papers feature structured and closed questions. **Unit 1: Biology 2** **Unit 2: Chemistry 2** **Unit 3: Physics 2**		Two papers Both papers feature structured and closed questions. **Unit 5:** **Additional Science 1** 1 h 30 min 90 marks 35% of GCSE Assesses: Biology 2 (B2.1 to B2.4) Chemistry 2 (C2.1 to C2.3) Physics 2 (P2.1 to P2.3) **Unit 6:** **Additional Science 2** 1 h 30 min 90 marks 40% of GCSE Assesses: Biology 2 (B2.5 to B2.8) Chemistry 2 (C2.4 to C2.7) Physics 2 (P2.4 to P2.6)
Unit 4: Controlled Assessment 1hr 35 min, plus time for research / data collection 50 marks 25% of GCSE		
1 Genetics	B2.7	B2.7
2 Cells and molecules	B2.1, B2.2, B2.5, B2.6, B2.7	B2.1, B2.2, B2.5, B2.6, B2.7
3 Sampling organisms	B2.3, B2.4	B2.3, B2.4
4 Physiology	B2.2, B2.5	B2.2, B2.5
5 Atoms and materials	C2.1, C2.2, C2.3, C2.6	C2.1, C2.2, C2.3, C2.6
6 Metals, tests and analysis	C2.1, C2.2, C2.3	C2.1, C2.2, C2.3
7 Salts and solubility	C2.6, C2.7	C2.6, C2.7
8 Calculation and physical chemistry	C2.3, C2.4, C2.5	C2.3, C2.4, C2.5
9 Forces and motion	P2.1, P2.2	P2.1, P2.2
10 Electricity	P2.3, P2.4	P2.3, P2.4
11 Radioactivity	P2.5, P2.6	

* There are tick charts throughout the book to show which particular sub-topics in each chapter are relevant to your course.

your GCSE course

Edexcel	OCR A	OCR B	WJEC
www.edexcel.com	www.ocr.org.uk	www.ocr.org.uk	www.wjec.co.uk
2SA01	J242	J262	600/0893/3
Three papers All papers: 1 hr 60 marks 25% of GCSE All papers feature objective, short answer and extended writing questions. **Unit B2** **Unit C2** **Unit P2**	Three papers All papers: 1 hr 60 marks 25% of GCSE All papers feature objective style and free response questions. **Modules B4, B5 and B6** **Modules C4, C5 and C6** **Modules P4, P5 and P6** OR **Modules B4, C4 and P4** **Modules B5, C5 and P5** **Modules B6, C6 and P6**	Two papers Both papers feature structured questions. **Modules B3, C3 and P3** 1hr 15 min 75 marks 35% of GCSE **Modules B4, C4 and P4** 1hr 30 min 85 marks 40% of GCSE Includes data analysis.	Three papers All papers: 1 hr 60 marks 25% of GCSE All papers feature structured questions involving some extended writing. **Biology 2** **Chemistry 2** **Physics 2**
Unit ASCA 3 hrs, plus approx. 6 hrs preparation time 50 marks 25% of GCSE	**Unit A154** Approx. 6-7hrs 64 marks 25% of GCSE	**Unit B723** Approx. 7 hrs 48 marks 25% of GCSE	**Unit CA** Approx. 7.5 hrs, plus time for initial research 48 marks 25% of GCSE
		B3	
B2	B4, B5	B3, B4	B2
B2	B4	B4	B2
B2		B3, B4	B2
C2	C4, C5, C6	C3, C4	C2
C2	C4, C5, C6	C3, C4	C2
C2	C5, C6	C4	C2
C2	C5, C6	C3	C2
P2	P4	P3	P2
P2	P5	P4	P2
P2	P6	P4	P2

5

Preparing for the exams

What will be assessed

In your science exams and controlled assessment you are assessed on three main criteria called assessment objectives:

- **Assessment Objective 1 (AO1)** – tests your ability to **recall**, select and communicate your knowledge and understanding of science
- **Assessment Objective 2 (AO2)** – tests your ability to **apply** your skills, knowledge and understanding of science in practical and other contexts
- **Assessment Objective 3 (AO3)** – tests your ability to **analyse** and **evaluate** evidence, make reasoned judgements and draw conclusions based on evidence

The exam papers have a lot of AO1 and AO2 questions and some AO3 questions. The controlled assessments focus mainly on AO2 and AO3.

To do well on the exams, it is not enough just to be able to recall facts. You must be able to apply your knowledge to different scenarios, analyse and evaluate evidence and formulate your own ideas and conclusions.

Planning your study

It is important to have an organised approach to study and revision throughout the course.

- After completing a topic in school or college, go through the topic again using this guide. Copy out the main points on a piece of paper or use a pen to highlight them.
- Much of memory is visual. Make sure your notes are laid out in a logical way using colour, charts, diagrams and symbols to present information in a visual way. If your notes are easy to read and attractive to the eye, they will be easier to remember.
- A couple of days, later try writing out the key points from memory. Check differences between what you wrote originally and what you wrote later.
- If you have written your notes on a piece of paper, make sure you keep them for revision later.
- Try some questions in the book and check your answers.
- Decide whether you have fully mastered the topic and write down any weaknesses you think you have.

How this book will help you

This complete study and revision guide will help you because...

- it contains the essential content for your GCSE course without the extra material that will not be examined.
- there are regular short progress checks so that you can test your understanding.
- it contains Sample GCSE questions with model answers and notes, so that you can see what the examiner is looking for.
- it contains Exam practice questions so that you can confirm your understanding and practise answering exam-style questions.
- the summary table on pages 4–5, and the exam-board signposting throughout the book, will ensure that only study and revise topics that are relevant to your course.

Six ways to improve your grade

1. Read the question carefully

Many students fail to answer the actual question set. Perhaps they misread the question or answer a similar question that they have seen before. Read the question once right through and then again more slowly. Underline key words in the question as you read through it. Questions at GCSE often contain a lot of information. You should be concerned if you are not using the information in your answer.

Take notice of the command words used in questions and make sure you answer appropriately:

- **State:** A concise, factual answer with no description or explanation
- **Describe:** A detailed answer that demonstrates knowledge of the facts about the topic
- **Explain:** A more detailed answer than a description; give reasons and use connectives like 'because'.
- **Calculate:** Give a numerical answer, including working and correct units
- **Suggest:** A personal response supported by facts.

2. Give enough detail

If a part of a question is worth three marks, you should make at least three separate points. Be careful that you do not make the same point three times, but worded in a slightly different way. Draw diagrams with a ruler and label with straight lines.

3. Be specific

Avoid using the word 'it' in your answers. Writing out in full what you are referring to will ensure the examiner knows what you are talking about. This is especially important in questions where you have to compare two or more things.

4. Use scientific language correctly

Try to use the correct scientific language in your answers. The way scientific language is used is often the difference between successful and unsuccessful students. As you revise, make a list of scientific terms you come across and check that you understand what they mean. Learn all the definitions. These are easy marks and they reward effort and good preparation.

5. Show your working

All science papers include calculations. Learn a set method for solving a calculation and use that method. You should always show your working in full. That way, if you make an arithmetical mistake, you may still receive marks for applying the correct science. Check your answer is given to the correct level of accuracy (significant figures or decimal places) and give the correct units.

6. Brush up on your writing skills

Your exam papers will include specific questions for which the answers will be marked on both scientific accuracy and the quality of the written communication. These questions are worth 6 marks, but it does not matter how good the science is, your answer will not gain full marks unless:

- the text is legible and the spelling, punctuation and grammar are accurate so that your meaning is clear
- you have used a form and style of writing that is fit for purpose and appropriate to the subject matter
- you have organised information in a clear and logical way, correctly using scientific vocabulary where appropriate.

These questions will be clearly indicated on the exam papers.

> Exam papers are scanned and marked on a computer screen. Do not write outside the answer spaces allowed, or your work may not be seen by the examiner. Ask for extra paper if you need it. Choose a black pen that will show up – one that photocopies well is a good choice.

How Science Works

The science GCSE courses are designed to help develop your knowledge of certain factual details, but also your understanding of 'How Science Works'.

'How Science Works' is essentially a set of key concepts that are relevant to all areas of science. It is concerned with four main areas:

Data, evidence, theories and explanations

- science as an evidence-based discipline
- the collaborative nature of science as a discipline and the way new scientific knowledge is validated
- how scientific understanding and theories develop
- the limitations of science
- how and why decisions about science and technology are made
- the use of modelling, including mathematical modelling, to explain aspects of science

Practical skills

- developing hypotheses
- planning practical ways to test hypotheses
- the importance of working accurately and safely
- identifying hazards and assessing risks
- collecting, processing, analysing and interpreting primary and secondary data
- reviewing methodology to assess fitness for purpose
- reviewing hypotheses in light of outcomes

Communication skills

- communicating scientific information using scientific, technical and mathematical language, conventions, and symbols.
- use models to explain systems, processes and abstract ideas

Applications and implications of science

- the ethical implications of science and its applications
- risk factors and risk assessment in the context of potential benefit

You will be taught about 'How Science Works' throughout the course in combination with the scientific content. Likewise, the different exam boards have included material about 'How Science Works' in different parts of their assessment.

'How Science Works' will be assessed in the controlled assessment, but you will also get questions that relate to it in the exams. If you come across questions about unfamiliar situations in the exam, do not panic and think that you have not learnt the work. Most of these questions are designed to test your skills and understanding of 'How Science Works', not your memory. The examiners want you to demonstrate what you know, understand and can do.

1 Genetics

The following topics are covered in this chapter:

- **Genes and chromosomes**
- **Passing on genes**
- **Gene technology**

1.1 Genes and chromosomes

LEARNING SUMMARY

After studying this section, you should be able to:
- explain what is meant by the term gene
- describe how sexual reproduction produces variation
- explain how sex is determined.

What is a gene?

EDEXCEL B2 ✓

Most cells contain a nucleus that controls all of the chemical reactions that go on in the cell. Nuclei can do this because they contain the genetic material. Genetic material controls the characteristics of an organism and is passed on from one generation to the next.

> **KEY POINT**
>
> The genetic material is made up of structures called chromosomes. They are made up of a chemical called **deoxyribonucleic acid** or **DNA**.

The DNA controls the cell by coding for the making of proteins, such as enzymes. The enzymes will control all the chemical reactions taking place in the cell.

> **KEY POINT**
>
> A **gene** is part of a chromosome that codes for one particular protein.

DNA codes for the proteins it makes by the order of four chemicals called **bases**. They are given the letters **A, C, G** and **T**. By controlling cells, genes therefore control all the characteristics of an organism.

Different organisms have different numbers of genes and different numbers of chromosomes. In most organisms that reproduce by sexual reproduction, the chromosomes can be arranged in pairs. This is because one of each pair comes from each parent.

Chromosomes and reproduction

No living organism can live forever so there is a need to reproduce.

> **KEY POINT**
>
> **Sexual reproduction** involves the passing on of genes from two parents to the offspring.

This is why we often look a little like both of our parents. The genes are passed on in the **sex cells** or **gametes** which join at **fertilisation**. In humans, each body cell has 46 chromosomes in 23 pairs. This means that when the male sex cells (sperm) are made they need to have 23 chromosomes, one from each pair. The female gametes (eggs) also need 23 chromosomes. When they join at fertilisation it will produce a cell called a **zygote** that has 46 chromosomes again. This will grow into an embryo and a baby. This also means that the offspring that are produced from sexual reproduction are all different because they have different combinations of chromosomes from their mother and father.

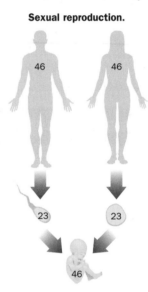

Sexual reproduction.

Because the baby can receive any one of the 23 pairs from mum and any one of the 23 pairs from dad, the number of possible gene combinations is enormous. This new mixture of genetic information produces a great deal of variation in the offspring. This just mixes genes up in different combinations, but the only way that new genes can be made is by **mutation**. This is a random change in a gene.

> You only need to know the number of chromosomes in a human cell. Do not worry if a question asks about a different animal. Look for what information it supplies, for example it might say that a sperm of a fruit fly has four chromosomes. You can then work out that a leg cell would have eight.

Sex determination

> **KEY POINT**
>
> In humans, the chromosomes of one of the 23 pairs are called the **sex chromosomes** because they carry the genes that determine the sex of the person.

There are two kinds of sex chromosome. One is called **X** and one is called **Y**.

- Females have two X chromosomes and are XX.
- Males have an X and a Y chromosome and are XY.

Females produce eggs that contain a single X chromosome and males produce sperm, half of which contain a Y chromosome and half of which contain an X chromosome. The diagram alongside shows the possible zygotes that can be produced by fertilisation.

The reason why the sex chromosomes determine the sex of a person is due to a single gene on the Y chromosome. This gene causes the production of testes rather than ovaries and so the male sex hormone testosterone is made. This will cause the development of all the male characteristics.

	X	Y
X	XX	XY
X	XX	XY

1.2 Passing on genes

LEARNING SUMMARY	After studying this section, you should be able to:
	• explain the difference between the terms dominant and recessive
	• explain the terms homozygous, heterozygous, genotype and phenotype
	• construct genetic diagrams to predict the results of crosses
	• recall the symptoms of certain genetic conditions
	• discuss the ethical issues arising from genetic screening.

Different copies of genes

AQA   B2   ✓

We have two copies of each chromosome in our cells (one from each parent). This therefore means that we have two copies of each gene. Sometimes the two copies are the same but sometimes they are different.

A good example of this is tongue rolling. This is controlled by a single gene and there are two possible copies of the gene, one that says roll and the other that says do not roll. If a person has one copy of each then they can still roll their tongue. This is because the copy for rolling is **dominant** and the non-rolling copy is **recessive**.

> **KEY POINT**
>
> Each copy of a gene is called an **allele**. If both alleles for a gene are the same this is called **homozygous**. **Heterozygous** means that the two alleles are different.

The only genes that cannot have two alleles present are those found on the X chromosome in men. This is because men only have one X chromosome. These genes are said to be **sex linked**.

The idea that characteristics were passed on as discrete 'factors' or genes was first suggested in 1866 by a monk called **Gregor Mendel**. At that time people believed that reproduction just caused factors to blend together. Using pea plants, Mendel showed that blending did not occur. At the time few scientists took any notice of his work because he was experimenting in a small monastery in the country. His work was rediscovered almost fifty years later.

We usually give the different copies (alleles) of a gene different letters, with the dominant copy a capital letter, for example T = tongue rolling and t = non-rolling.

Let us assume that Mum cannot roll her tongue, but Dad can. Both of Dad's alleles are T so he is homozygous. This is called his **genotype** as it describes what alleles he has. Rolling his tongue is called his **phenotype** as it describes the effect of the alleles. The cross is usually drawn out like this:

		Mum	
		t	t
Dad	T	Tt	Tt
	T	Tt	Tt

← All are tongue rollers

In this cross all the children can roll their tongue.

If both Mum and Dad are heterozygous the children that can produce will be different:

> If you have to choose which letters to use in a cross, make sure that you use capital and small versions of the same letter and choose a letter that looks different in the two versions. Avoid **C** and **c** or **S** and **s**!

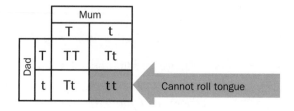

Cannot roll tongue

In this cross, 1 in 4 or 25% or a quarter of the children cannot roll their tongue.

Genetic disorders

AQA   B2   ✓

Many **genetic disorders** are caused by certain copies of genes. These can be passed on from mother or father to the baby and lead to the baby having the disorder. Examples of these disorders are cystic fibrosis, Huntington's disease and sickle-cell anaemia. People with these disorders become ill.

Cystic fibrosis	Huntington's disease	Sickle-cell anaemia
Caused by a recessive allele	Caused by a dominant allele	Caused by a recessive allele
Symptoms include: • thick mucus collects in the lung • breathing is difficult • chest infections • food is not properly digested.	Symptoms include: • muscle twitching (tremor) • loss of memory • difficulty in controlling movements • mood changes.	Symptoms include: • feeling tired or weak • coldness in the hands and feet • pain in the bones, lungs and joints

By looking at family trees of these genetic disorders and drawing genetic diagrams (such as the one for tongue rolling) it is possible for people to know the chance of them having a child with a genetic disorder. This may leave them with a difficult decision to make as to whether to have children or not.

Genetic screening

AQA   B2   ✓

Genetic cross diagrams can only work out the probability of a child being affected. It is now possible to test cells directly to see if they contain an allele for a particular genetic disorder. This is called **genetic screening**. This could be done at different stages:

- In an **adult**. This could tell the person if they are a carrier for the disorder and so if they may be able to pass it on. It could also tell if the person was going to develop a certain disorder later in life, for example Huntington's disease.
- In a **foetus**. Some cells can be taken from the foetus whilst the mother is pregnant. The parents can then find out if their baby will have the genetic disorder.
- In an **embryo** before it is implanted in the mother. If an embryo is produced by IVF outside the mother's body, then it can be tested before it is implanted in the mother. It is therefore possible to choose which embryos to put into the mother.

> To get an A*, you must be able to describe arguments for and against genetic screening in a particular situation. Make sure you give both views.

The process of genetic screening brings with it some difficult ethical decisions:

- In an adult would you want to know if you were going to develop a disease from which there is no cure? Should your employer or your insurance company be told?
- In a foetus the parents could have to decide whether to have a termination or not.
- In an embryo the test is called **preimplantation genetic diagnosis**. Some people think that the destruction of early embryos is wrong. Others worry that the embryos may be tested and chosen for characteristics other than those involving disorders.

PROGRESS CHECK

1. Why can a person roll their tongue even if their cells have an allele for non-rolling?
2. Name a genetic disorder caused by a dominant allele.
3. What is the difference between genotype and phenotype?
4. What is genetic screening?
5. What is the difference between a gene and an allele?
6. Suggest why people may not want their insurance company or employer to have the results of their genetic screening.

6. They may not get insurance or the job they apply for if people know that they will develop a genetic disease in the future.
5. A gene is a length of DNA that codes for a protein, an allele is a particular copy of a gene that codes for a particular variation of the protein.
4. Testing for a genetic disease.
3. Genotype is what alleles a person has and phenotype is how the alleles express themselves (the characteristics of the person).
2. Huntington's disease.
1. The allele for rolling is dominant over the allele for non-rolling.

1.3 Gene technology

> **LEARNING SUMMARY**
>
> After studying this section, you should be able to:
> - describe how plants can reproduce asexually
> - describe how animals can be cloned
> - describe the possible medical uses of stem cells
> - discuss some of the uses and issues arising from genetic engineering

Cloning

| OCR B | B3 | ✓ |
| EDEXCEL | B2 | ✓ |

KEY POINT

Bacteria, plants and some animals can reproduce **asexually**. This only needs one parent and does not involve sex cells joining.

All the offspring that are made are genetically identical to the parent.

Gardeners often use **asexual reproduction** to copy plants – they know what the offspring will look like.

Different organisms have different ways of reproducing asexually:

- The spider plant grows new plantlets on the end of long shoots.
- Daffodil plants produce lots of smaller bulbs that can grow into new plants.
- Strawberry plants grow long runners that touch the ground and grow a new plant.

Asexual reproduction produces organisms that have the same genes as the parent.

How Dolly was produced from a cloned cell.

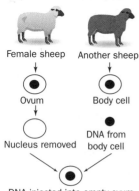

Female sheep   Another sheep

↓   ↓

Ovum   Body cell

↓   ↓

Nucleus removed   DNA from body cell

DNA injected into empty ovum

↓

Ovum returned to female sheep

↓

Grows into Dolly

 Dolly

> **KEY POINT**
>
> Genetically identical individuals are called **clones.**

Many plants, such as the spider plant, clone themselves naturally and it is easy for a gardener to **take cuttings** to make identical plants. Modern methods involve **tissue culture** which uses small groups of cells taken from plants to grow new plants.

Cloning animals is much harder to do. Two main methods are used:

- **Cloning embryos** where embryos are split up at an early stage and the cells are put into host mothers to grow.
- **Cloning adult cells.** The first mammal to be cloned from adult cells was Dolly the sheep.

Since Dolly was born other animals have been cloned and there has been much interest about cloning humans.

> Remember that clones have the same genes so any differences between them must be due to their environment.

There could be two possible reasons for cloning humans:

- **Reproductive cloning** to make embryos for infertile couples.
- **Therapeutic cloning** to produce embryos that can be used to treat diseases.

Stem cells

AQA	B2	✓
OCR B	B3	✓
EDEXCEL	B2	✓

The use of embryos to treat disease is possible due to the discovery of **stem cells**.

> **KEY POINT**
>
> Stem cells are cells that can divide to make all the different tissues in the body.

They can be extracted from cloned embryos. Scientists think that they could be used to repair damaged tissues such as injuries to the spinal cord.

There are therefore many different views about cloning:

Both infertility and genetic disease cause much pain and distress. I think that we should be able to use cloning to treat these problems.

It is not right to clone people because clones are not true individuals and it is not right to destroy embryos to supply stem cells.

There are two main types of stem cells:

- **Embryonic stem cells** can develop into any type of cell. It is easy to extract them from an embryo, but the embryo is destroyed as a result.
- **Adult stem cells** can develop into a limited range of cell types. It is not necessary to destroy an embryo to get them, but they are difficult to find.

Genetic engineering

OCR B   B3   ✓
EDEXCEL   B2   ✓

All living organisms use the same language of DNA. The four letters A, G, C and T are the same in all living things. Therefore a gene from one organism can be removed and placed in a totally different organism where it will continue to carry out its function. This means, for example, a cow will use a human gene to make the same protein that a human would make.

> **KEY POINT**
>
> Moving a gene from one organism to another is called **genetic engineering**.

Genetic engineering.

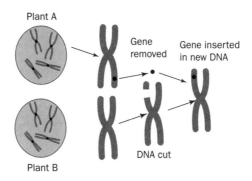

There is also the possibility that genetic engineering may be used to treat genetic disorders like cystic fibrosis. Scientists are trying to replace the genes in people that have the disorder with working genes.

> **KEY POINT**
>
> Using genetic engineering to treat genetic disorders is called **gene therapy**.

GM crops

OCR B   B3   ✓

New **genetically modified (GM)** plants can be made in this way so that they:

- may be more resistant to insects eating them
- can be resistant to herbicides (weed killers)
- can produce a higher yield.

People often have different views about GM crops. Views against GM crops include:

- Genetic engineering is against 'God and Nature'.
- There may be long-term health problems with eating GM crops.
- Pollen from GM crops may spread to wild crops.

Views for GM crops include:

- More food to supply starving populations.
- Less need to spray harmful insecticides and herbicides.

PROGRESS CHECK

1. Why does a gardener use cuttings rather than seeds to reproduce an attractive plant?
2. What was Dolly?
3. What can stem cells do that normal body cells cannot?
4. Write down one characteristic that is chosen for GM crops.
5. Many people think that using adult stem cells to treat disease is acceptable, but are against using embryonic stem cells. Suggest why this is.
6. Suggest why farmers might want a crop that is resistant to herbicides.

6. They can spray their whole field with weedkiller, killing all the weeds, except the crop.
5. Use of embryonic stem cells involves the destruction of an embryo, but using adult stem cells does not. Some people consider an embryo to be an individual life.
4. Resistance to insects eating them/resistance to herbicides/produce a higher yield.
3. They can differentiate into any other type of cell.
2. Dolly was a sheep and the first mammal that was produced by cloning from an adult cell.
1. Cuttings will produce an identical copy so the gardener can be sure of the characteristic of the plant.

Sample GCSE questions

1 Read the following passage carefully and use it to help you answer the questions.

> Albinism is a condition that causes a person to produce very little coloured pigment in their skin, hair or iris. This means that they have white hair, pink irises and very pale skin.
>
> The condition is not usually life threatening if the person takes some simple precautions. Albinism causes the person to become sun burnt very easily and the action of ultraviolet light on the skin is more likely to cause mutations.
>
> The condition is caused by a recessive allele (a). The dominant allele (A) causes normal pigment production.

(a) The action of ultraviolet light on the skin causes mutations.

What are mutations? [1]

Random changes in genes.

(b) Suggest one 'simple precaution' that a person with albinism might take. [1]

Wear sun block when outdoors.

(c) The allele that causes albinism is said to be recessive. Explain what this means. [2]

A recessive allele does not express itself if the dominant allele is present. Only people who have a homozygous recessive genotype will be albino.

(d) Explain how two parents who do not have albinism can produce a child that does have albinism.

Use a genetic diagram to help you. [4]

If both parents have heterozygous genotypes (Aa), there is a 25% chance that their child will be albino (aa).

		Mum	
		A	a
Dad	A	AA	Aa
	a	Aa	aa

You would also get the mark for this question if you said 'DNA' instead of 'genes'.

If a question asks you to 'suggest' something, there will be more than one possible answer. As long as you consider the facts and give a sensible answer, you will get the mark. Alternative answers could have been: 'wear sunglasses' or 'do not go out in bright sunshine'.

This question is worth two marks, so the examiner is looking for you to make two clear points. Make sure you can use scientific terms relating to genetics correctly.

To get full marks on this type of question you must state the genotypes of the two parents, the individual gametes and the four possible outcomes. You must also identify which outcome would result in an albino child. Make sure your diagram is clear and neat.

Exam practice questions

1 **(a)** Peter and Kirsten are expecting a baby.

They know that it has an even chance of being a boy or a girl.

Finish the genetic diagram to show why this is.

Kirsten

Gametes	X	X

Peter

[2]

(b) The table shows the ratio of males to females in different countries and at different ages.

Age	India	Kenya	Russia	UK
at birth	1.12	1.02	1.06	1.05
over 65 years old	0.91	0.83	0.44	0.76
all ages	1.08	1.01	0.85	0.98

(i) In which countries do women live longer than men?

Use data from the table to justify your answer.

....

.... [2]

(ii) In some countries parents want to have baby boys rather than girls.

Embryos can be tested to see what sex they are before they are born.

People are worried that this technique might be used to terminate female embryos.

In which country would the data in the table suggest this is possibly happening?

Use data from the table to justify your answer.

....

....

.... [2]

(iii) Suggest **one** reason why people might be concerned about the effect on the country of the termination of female embryos.

....

.... [1]

2 Cells and molecules

The following topics are covered in this chapter:

- Cells and organisation
- DNA and protein synthesis
- Proteins and enzymes
- Cell division
- Growth and development
- Transport in cells
- Respiration

2.1 Cells and organisation

LEARNING SUMMARY

After studying this section you should be able to:

- describe the differences between plant and animal cells
- describe the fine detail of cells that can be seen with the electron microscope
- describe the levels of organisation found in multicellular organisms
- describe the structure of a typical bacterial cell.

Plant and animal cells

AQA	B2	✓
OCR A	B4	✓
OCR B	B3	✓
EDEXCEL	B2	✓
WJEC	B2	✓

Plants and animal cells have a number of structures in common. They all have:

- A **nucleus** that carries genetic information and controls the cell.
- A **cell membrane** which controls the movement of substances in and out of the cell.
- **Cytoplasm** where most of the chemical reactions happen.

There are three main differences between plant and animal cells:

- Plant cells have a strong **cell wall** made of cellulose, whereas animal cells do not. The cell wall supports the cell and stops it bursting.
- Plant cells have a large permanent **vacuole** containing cell sap, but vacuoles in animal cells are small and temporary. The cell sap is under pressure and this supports the plant.

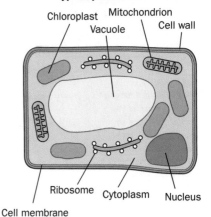

Typical plant cell.

Chloroplast   Mitochondrion
Vacuole   Cell wall

Ribosome   Cytoplasm   Nucleus

Cell membrane

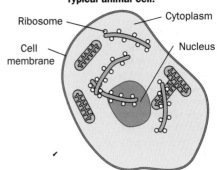

Typical animal cell.

Ribosome   Cytoplasm

Cell membrane   Nucleus

- Plant cells may contain **chloroplasts** containing chlorophyll for photosynthesis. Animal cells never contain chloroplasts.

To get an A*, you must be able to measure cells and structures from a drawing and then use the magnification of the drawing to work out their size in real life. Remember that magnification = image size/size in real life.

The naked eye can see detail down to about 0.1 mm. Cells are smaller than this so a microscope is needed to see individual cells. The best **light microscopes** can magnify cells so that objects as small as 0.002 mm can be seen clearly. At this magnification other structures in the cell become visible, but cannot be seen clearly. Using an **electron microscope** allows objects as small as 0.000002 mm to be seen:

- **Mitochondria** are the site of respiration in the cell.
- **Ribosomes** are small structures in the cytoplasm where proteins are made.

A mitochondrium.

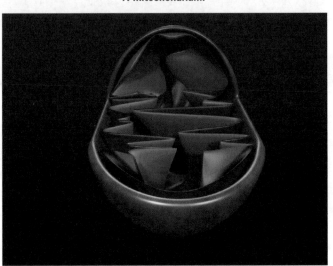

Levels of organisation

AQA	B2	✓
OCR A	B5	✓
OCR B	B3	✓
EDEXCEL	B2	✓

Some organisms are made of one cell. They are **unicellular**. There seems to be a limit in the size of a single cell so larger organisms are made up of a number of cells. They are **multicellular**. The cells are not all alike, but are specialised for particular jobs, for example guard cells in leaves, and neurones.

Similar cells, doing similar jobs, are gathered together into **tissues** such as xylem and nerve. Different tissues are gathered together into **organs** to do a particular job, for example leaves and the brain.

Groups of organs often work together in **systems** to carry out related functions.

Make sure that you can remember the order of terms to describe the levels of organisation: Cells, Tissues, Organs, Systems. Think of a way of remembering this.

Be careful with 'bone' and 'muscle'. Bone and muscle are both tissues. However 'a bone' and 'a muscle' are both organs as they contain a number of different tissues.

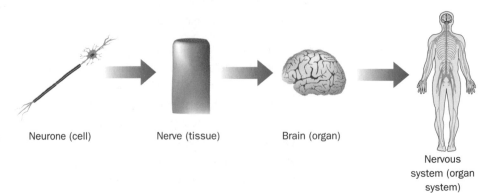

Neurone (cell)   Nerve (tissue)   Brain (organ)   Nervous system (organ system)

Challenges for multicellular organisms

AQA	B2	✓
OCR B	B3	✓
WJEC	B2	✓

Becoming larger and multicellular does have some advantages. For example, it allows cells to specialise. This makes them more efficient at their job. However, it also produces difficulties.

The difficulties that need to be solved are:

- It requires a communication system between cells to be developed.
- It is harder to supply all the cells with nutrients.
- The surface area to volume ratio is smaller so it is harder to exchange substances with the environment.

Structure of bacteria

AQA	B2	✓
OCR A	B4	✓
OCR B	B3	✓
EDEXCEL	B2	✓
WJEC	B2	✓

Bacterial cells are very different to plant and animal cells. That is why they are classified in a different kingdom (prokaryotes). They vary in shape, but all bacterial cells have a similar structure.

A generalised bacterium.

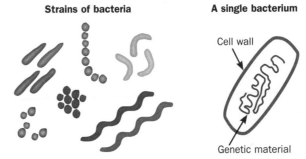

Strains of bacteria   A single bacterium

Cell wall

Genetic material

Bacterial cells are smaller than animal and plant cells. They lack a true nucleus, mitochondria, chloroplasts and vacuoles.

PROGRESS CHECK

1. Write down three structures that are found in plant cells, but not in animal cells.
2. Why is cell sap important to the structure of a plant?
3. At what level of organisation are leaves and the brain?
4. Where is DNA found in a bacterium?
5. Specialisation allows cells to become more efficient at their particular role. A disadvantage of specialisation is that an organism cannot live if it loses certain organs. Suggest why this is.

5. The cells become so specialised that they cannot take on other roles and take the function of those lost.
4. In the cytoplasm.
3. Organs.
2. Cell sap in the vacuole is under pressure and so supports the plant.
1. Cell wall, vacuole, chloroplasts.

2.2 DNA and protein synthesis

LEARNING SUMMARY

After studying this section you should be able to:

- describe the structure of DNA and how it was discovered
- explain how DNA codes for proteins
- describe the process of protein synthesis.

The structure of DNA

AQA	B2	✓
OCR A	B5	✓
OCR B	B3	✓
EDEXCEL	B2	✓
WJEC	B2	✓

The nucleus controls the chemical reactions occurring in the cell. This is because it contains the genetic material. This is contained in structures called **chromosomes** which are made of **DNA**. DNA is a large molecule with a very important structure:

- It has two strands.
- The strands are twisted to make a shape called a **double helix**.
- Each strand is made of a long chain of molecules including sugar, phosphates and bases.
- There are only four bases called A, C, G and T.
- Links between the bases hold the two chains together, C always links with G and A with T.

The DNA helix.

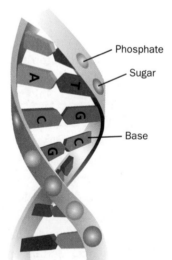

Phosphate

Sugar

Base

> You need to remember <u>A</u> with <u>T</u> and <u>C</u> with <u>G</u>. Find a way of remembering it that means something to you. It could be <u>Auntie</u> <u>T</u>ina and <u>C</u>ousin <u>G</u>eorge for example.

Discovering the structure of DNA

| OCR B | B3 | ✓ |
| EDEXCEL | B2 | ✓ |

KEY POINT

The two scientists that are famous for discovering the structure of DNA are Francis Crick and James Watson.

'How Science Works' questions may ask for examples of how advances in science are made by cooperation between scientists. The discovery of the structure of DNA is a good example to use.

They worked together in Cambridge in the early 1950s. A molecule of DNA is only about 0.00000034 mm wide, so they could not use a microscope to see it! This is where they needed information obtained by other scientists:

- Maurice Wilkins and Rosalind Franklin fired X-rays at DNA crystals and the images they obtained told Watson and Crick that DNA was shaped like a helix, with two chains.
- Erwin Chargaff had worked out that there was always the same percentage of the base C as G and the same percentage of A as T.

These two pieces of information allowed Watson and Crick to build their famous model of the structure.

Coding for proteins

AQA	B2	✓
OCR A	B5	✓
OCR B	B3	✓
EDEXCEL	B2	✓
WJEC	B2	✓

KEY POINT

DNA controls the cell by carrying the code for proteins.

- Each different protein is made of a particular order of amino acids, so DNA must code for this order.
- A gene is a length of DNA that codes for the order of amino acids in one protein.

Scientists now know that each amino acid in a protein is coded for by each set of three bases along the DNA molecule.

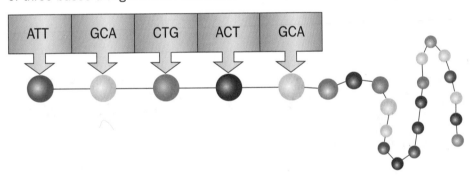

Protein synthesis

AQA	B2	✓
OCR A	B5	✓
OCR B	B3	✓
EDEXCEL	B2	✓
WJEC	B2	✓

KEY POINT

Proteins are made on **ribosomes** in the cytoplasm and DNA is kept in the nucleus and cannot leave.

The cell has to use a messenger molecule to copy the message from DNA and to carry the code to the ribosomes. This molecule is called **messenger RNA (mRNA)**. When a protein is to be made these steps occur:

The word complementary is a useful word to use when describing mRNA. It does not 'copy' the code exactly, but makes a version using the matching bases.

- The DNA containing that gene unwinds and 'unzips'.
- Complementary mRNA molecules pair up next to the DNA bases on one strand.
- The mRNA units join together and make a molecule with a complementary copy of the gene. This is called **transcription.**
- The mRNA molecule then leaves the nucleus and attaches to a ribosome.
- The base code on the mRNA is then used to link amino acids together in the correct order to produce the protein. Each three bases code for one amino acid. This is called **translation.**

2.3 Proteins and enzymes

LEARNING SUMMARY

After studying this section you should be able to:

- describe the main functions of proteins
- explain how enzymes work
- explain why enzymes are affected by extremes of temperature and pH.

The functions of proteins

AQA	B2	✓
OCR B	B3	✓

The only way that the genetic material can control the cell is by coding for which proteins are made. The proteins that are produced have a wide range of different functions:

- Structural proteins used to build cells, e.g. collagen.
- Hormones to carry messages, e.g. insulin.
- Carrier molecules, e.g. haemoglobin.
- Enzymes to speed up reactions, e.g. amylase.

Enzymes

AQA	B2	✓
OCR A	B4	✓
OCR B	B3	✓
EDEXCEL	B2	✓
WJEC	B2	✓

> **KEY POINT**
>
> **Enzymes are biological catalysts.**

Many people think that all enzymes are released into the gut to digest food. Remember that most enzymes are found inside cells and are never released.

They are produced in all living organisms and control all the chemical reactions that occur. Most of the chemical reactions that occur in living organisms would occur too slowly without enzymes. Increased temperatures would speed up the reactions, but using enzymes means that the reactions are fast enough at 37°C. These reactions include DNA replication, digestion, photosynthesis, respiration and protein synthesis.

How do enzymes work?

AQA	B2	✓
OCR A	B4	✓
OCR B	B3	✓
EDEXCEL	B2	✓
WJEC	B2	✓

As enzymes are protein molecules they are made of a long chain of amino acids that is folded up to make a particular shape.

KEY POINT

They have a slot or a groove, called the **active site**, into which the **substrate** fits.

The substrate is the substance that is going to react. The reaction then takes place and the **products** leave the enzyme. This explanation for how enzymes work is called the **Lock and Key theory**.

The substrate fits into the active site like a key fitting into a lock.

KEY POINT

Enzymes work best at a particular temperature and pH. This is called the **optimum** temperature or pH.

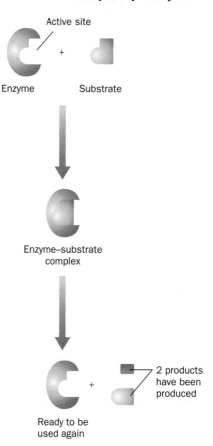

The Lock and Key theory of enzymes.

Active site

Enzyme + Substrate

Enzyme–substrate complex

2 products have been produced

Ready to be used again

Enzymes have different optimum pH values that depend on where they usually work.

How temperature and substrate concentration affect reaction rate.

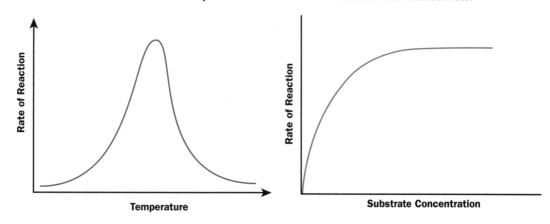

If the concentration of the substrate is increased then the reaction will be faster up to a certain concentration and then it will level off until all the enzymes are working at their maximum rate. At this point increasing the substrate concentration does not increase the rate of reaction.

Enzyme properties

AQA	B2	✓
OCR A	B4	✓
OCR B	B3	✓
EDEXCEL	B2	✓
WJEC	B2	✓

The Lock and Key theory can be used to explain many of the properties of enzymes:

- It explains why an enzyme will only work on one type of substrate. They are described as **specific**. The substrate has to be the right shape to fit into the active site.
- If the temperature is too low, then the substrate and the enzyme molecules will not collide so often and the reaction will slow down. If the shape of the enzyme molecule changes, then the substrate will not easily fit into the active site. This means that the reaction will slow down. High temperatures and extremes of pH may cause this to happen.

Many candidates lose marks by saying that heat kills enzymes. Remember that enzymes are protein molecules and not living organisms. Say that they are denatured or destroyed, but not killed!

KEY POINT

If the shape of the enzyme molecule is irreversibly changed then it is described as being **denatured**.

PROGRESS CHECK

1. Why does a lack of protein stunt growth?
2. Why are enzymes necessary in living organisms?
3. What is the lock and what is the key in the Lock and Key theory?
4. What does the phrase 'optimum temperature' mean?
5. Lipase digests fats, but it will not digest proteins. Explain why this is.
6. Adding vinegar to food can stop the food being digested and spoilt by bacteria and fungi. Explain why this is.

1. Proteins are needed to make key structures inside the body, e.g. bone and so without protein growth will be limited.
2. To allow reactions to be fast enough at body temperature.
3. The lock is the enzyme's active site and the key is the substrate.
4. The temperature at which the reaction occurs at the fastest rate.
5. Lipase has a particular shaped active site that fats will fit into, but not proteins.
6. Vinegar is acidic and so the pH would be too low so the enzymes of the decay organisms would not work.

2.4 Cell division

LEARNING SUMMARY

After studying this section you should be able to:

- describe how DNA is copied
- explain the main differences between mitosis and meiosis
- describe the main sources of genetic variation.

Copying DNA

AQA	B2	✓
OCR A	B5	✓
OCR B	B3	✓
WJEC	B2	✓

Before a cell divides two things must happen. Firstly, new cell organelles such as mitochondria must be made. Secondly, the DNA must copy itself. Watson and Crick realised that the structure of DNA allows this to happen in a rather neat way:

- The double helix of DNA unwinds and the two strands come apart or 'unzip'.
- The bases on each strand attract their complementary bases and so two new molecules are made.

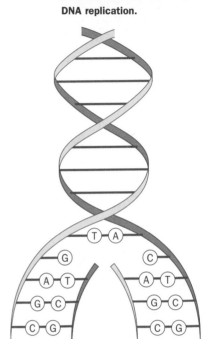

DNA replication.

Types of cell division

AQA	B2	✓
OCR A	B5	✓
OCR B	B3	✓
EDEXCEL	B2	✓
WJEC	B2	✓

Cells divide for a number of reasons. There are two types of cell division – **meiosis** and **mitosis** – and they are used for different reasons.

In most questions you will not lose marks if your spelling is a little inaccurate. However, make sure that you spell mitosis and meiosis correctly or the examiner may not know which one you mean.

Edexcel candidates need to be able to describe how the sex cells produced by meiosis are adapted for their functions.

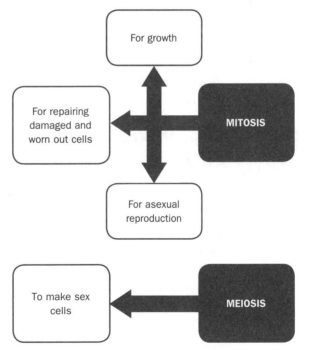

Mitosis

AQA	B2	✓
OCR A	B5	✓
OCR B	B3	✓
EDEXCEL	B2	✓
WJEC	B2	✓

In mitosis, two cells are produced from one. As long as the chromosomes have been copied exactly then each new cell will have the same number of chromosomes and therefore the same genetic information as each other and the parent cell.

Mitosis.

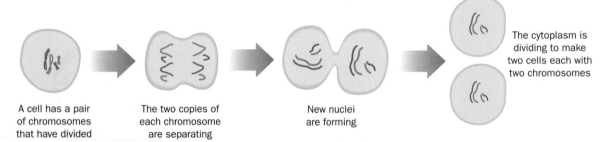

A cell has a pair of chromosomes that have divided

The two copies of each chromosome are separating

New nuclei are forming

The cytoplasm is dividing to make two cells each with two chromosomes

Meiosis

AQA	B2	✓
OCR A	B5	✓
OCR B	B3	✓
EDEXCEL	B2	✓
WJEC	B2	✓

In meiosis, the chromosomes are also copied once, but the cell divides twice. This makes four cells each with half the number of chromosomes, one from each pair.

Meiosis.

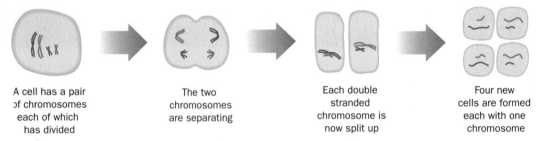

A cell has a pair of chromosomes each of which has divided

The two chromosomes are separating

Each double stranded chromosome is now split up

Four new cells are formed each with one chromosome

Cells with one chromosome from each pair are called **haploid** and can be used as **gametes**. When two gametes join at fertilisation, the **diploid** or full number of chromosomes is produced.

Variation and mutation

| OCR B | B3 | ✓ |
| EDEXCEL | B2 | ✓ |

When DNA is copied, before mitosis and meiosis occur, mistakes are sometimes made.

> **KEY POINT**
>
> A **gene mutation** occurs when one of the chemical bases in DNA is changed.

This may mean that a different amino acid is coded for and this can change the protein that is made. When this happens, it is most unlikely to benefit the organism. Either the protein will not be made at all or most likely it will not work properly. Very occasionally, a mutation may be useful and without mutations we would not be here. Mutations occur randomly at a very low rate, but some factors can make them happen more often.

These include:

- ultraviolet in sun light
- X-rays
- chemical mutagens as found in, for example, cigarettes.

Only mutations can produce new genes, but meiosis can recombine them in different orders. Also as a baby can receive any one of the chromosomes in each pair from the mother and any one from the father, the number of possible gene combinations is enormous. This new mixture of genetic information produces a great deal of variation in the offspring. This is why meiosis and sexual reproduction produces so much more variation than asexual reproduction.

> Remember that mitosis can produce cells that are genetically different, but this only happens if there is a mutation. Otherwise, they are genetically identical. Meiosis always produces genetic variation.

PROGRESS CHECK

1. Does a new molecule of DNA have none, one or two original strands?
2. Where in the human body does meiosis occur?
3. The haploid number of chromosomes in humans is 23. What is the diploid number?
4. Write down two differences between mitosis and meiosis.
5. Why is a gene mutation often harmful?
6. Why is it important to make sure that your sunglasses filter out UV light?

6. UV light can be absorbed by DNA and cause mutations.
5. It usually produces a new protein that does not work as well.
4. Meiosis introduces more variation; meiosis makes four cells but mitosis makes two; meiosis makes cells with half the number of chromosomes but mitosis produces cells that have the same number as the parent cells.
3. 46
2. In the ovaries and testes.
1. One.

2.5 Growth and development

<table>
<tr><td rowspan="7">**LEARNING SUMMARY**</td><td>**After studying this section you should be able to:**</td></tr>
<tr><td>• recall the meaning of the term differentiation</td></tr>
<tr><td>• explain the function of stem cells</td></tr>
<tr><td>• describe the main parts of a human growth curve</td></tr>
<tr><td>• describe how different parts of the body grow at different rates</td></tr>
<tr><td>• describe the differences between plant growth and animal growth</td></tr>
<tr><td>• describe ways of measuring growth.</td></tr>
</table>

Division and differentiation

AQA	B2	✓
OCR A	B5	✓
OCR B	B3	✓
EDEXCEL	B2	✓
WJEC	B2	✓

KEY POINT

When gametes join at fertilisation this produces a single cell called a **zygote**.

The zygote soon starts to divide many times by mitosis to produce many identical cells. These cells then start to become specialised for different jobs.

> **KEY POINT**
>
> The production of different types of cells for different jobs is called **differentiation**.

These differentiated cells can then form tissues and organs.

Stem cells

AQA	B2	✓
OCR A	B5	✓
OCR B	B3	✓
EDEXCEL	B2	✓
WJEC	B2	✓

Some cells in the embryo and in the adult keep the ability to form other types of cells. They are called **stem cells**. Scientists are now trying to use stem cells to replace cells that have stopped working or been damaged. This may have the potential to cure a number of conditions.

Uses of stem cells

AQA	B2	✓
OCR A	B5	✓
OCR B	B3	✓
EDEXCEL	B2	✓
WJEC	B2	✓

Once a cell has differentiated it does not form other types of cells. Although it has the same genes as all the other cells, many are turned off so it only makes the proteins it needs. Scientists have found a way to switch genes back on and so have been able to clone animals from body cells. This is covered on page 14.

This means that it is now possible to produce embryos that are clones of an animal and to use them to supply embryonic stem cells. There are many different views about the possibility of cloning humans to obtain stem cells.

Human growth curves

| OCR B | B3 | ✓ |
| EDEXCEL | B2 | ✓ |

Humans grow at different rates at different parts of their lives. This is shown in the graph.

The graph shows that there are two phases of rapid growth, one just after birth and the other in adolescence.

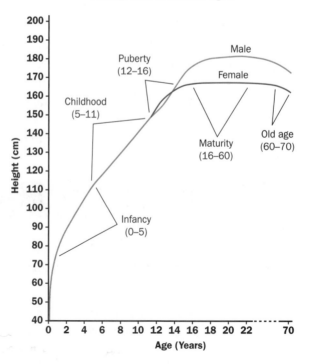

Human growth at different ages.

Growth of different parts of the body

OCR B   B3   ✓

The various parts of the body also grow at different rates at different times.

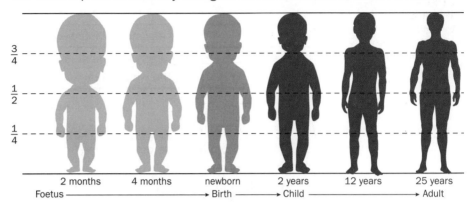

The diagram shows that the head and brain of an early foetus grow very quickly compared to the rest of the body. Later, the body and legs start to grow faster and the brain and head growth slows down into puberty and adulthood.

Plant growth

OCR A   B5   ✓
OCR B   B3   ✓
EDEXCEL B2   ✓

Like animals, plants grow by making new cells by mitosis. The cells then differentiate into tissues like xylem and phloem. These tissues then form organs such as roots, leaves and flowers.

Growth in plants is different to animal growth in a number of ways:

- Plant cells enlarge much more than animal cells after they are produced. This increases the size of the plant.
- Cells tend to divide at the ends of roots and shoots. This means that plants grow from their tips.
- Animals usually stop growing when they reach a certain size, but plants carry on growing.
- Many plant cells keep the ability to produce new types of cells, but in animals only stem cells can do this. Plant cells that can produce new types of cells are called **meristematic**.

Measuring growth

OCR B   B3   ✓
EDEXCEL B2   ✓

Growth can be measured as an increase in **height**, **wet mass** or **dry mass**.

> **KEY POINT**
>
> Dry mass is the best measure of growth.

There are advantages and disadvantages of measuring growth by each method.

Measurement	Advantage	Disadvantage
Length or height	Easy to measure	Only measures growth in one direction
Wet mass	Fairly easy to measure	Water content can vary
Dry mass	Measures permanent growth over the whole body	Involves removing all the water from an organism

PROGRESS CHECK

1. Write down one type of specialised cell.
2. What is a stem cell?
3. Look at the human growth curve. What does it show about growth in old age?
4. Which parts of a plant contain the main growth areas?
5. Suggest why the head is much larger than the rest of the body when the baby is young.
6. Using dry mass to measure the growth of an organism presents a number of difficulties. Suggest what these difficulties are.

1. Example: Muscle cell.
2. A cell that has not yet differentiated and so can divide to produce any type of cell.
3. Growth becomes negative, i.e. more cells are dying than are being produced.
4. The meristems at the tips of the roots and shoots.
5. The brain needs to develop first to control the other parts of the body.
6. This is destructive and it is difficult to tell when it has all been removed. The organism has to be killed and all water removed in order to measure dry mass. Therefore it is hard to get an idea of growth over time.

2.6 Transport in cells

LEARNING SUMMARY

After studying this section you should be able to:

- describe the processes of diffusion, osmosis and active transport
- explain the importance of osmosis in supporting plants
- describe how to demonstrate osmosis in plant tissue.

Diffusion

AQA	B2	✓
OCR A	B4	✓
OCR B	B4	✓
EDEXCEL	B2	✓
WJEC	B2	✓

KEY POINT

Diffusion is the movement of a substance from an area of high concentration to an area of low concentration.

Diffusion works because particles are always moving about in a random way. The rate of diffusion can be increased in a number of ways:

Factors that increase diffusion rate.

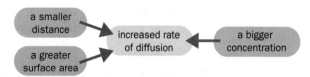

Osmosis

OCR A	B4	✓
OCR B	B4	✓
EDEXCEL	B2	✓
WJEC	B2	✓

Osmosis is really a special type of diffusion. It involves the diffusion of water.

> **KEY POINT**
>
> Osmosis is the movement of water across a partially permeable membrane from an area of high water concentration to an area of low water concentration.

The cell membrane is an example of a partially permeable membrane. It lets small molecules through, such as water, but stops larger molecules, such as glucose.

Osmosis.

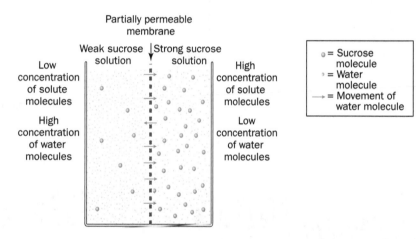

Osmosis and support in plants

| OCR B | B4 | ✓ |
| WJEC | B3 | ✓ |

When plant cells gain water by osmosis, they swell. The cell wall stops them from bursting. This makes the cell stiff or **turgid**. If a plant cell loses water it goes limp or **flaccid**.

Osmosis in plant cells.

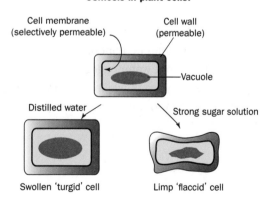

Turgid cells are very important in helping to support plants. Plants with flaccid cells often wilt. Sometimes the cells may lose so much water that the cell membrane may come away from the cell wall. This is called **plasmolysis**.

Animal cells do not behave in the same way because they do not have a cell wall. They will either swell up and burst if they gain water, or shrink if they lose water.

Demonstrating osmosis

OCR A	B4	✓
OCR B	B4	✓
EDEXCEL	B2	✓
WJEC	B2	✓

It is possible to show how osmosis has occurred by cutting cylinders out of potato and putting them into sugar solutions of different concentrations. If the mass of the chips is taken before and after they are put in the solutions a graph like this can be plotted:

Make sure you can explain the shape of this graph. It might be drawn as the length of the potato chip rather than the mass. It's just the same.

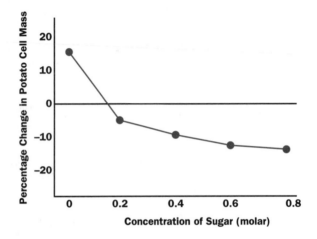

In less concentrated solutions the potato gains water and increases in mass. At high concentrations of sugar the potato loses water and decreases in mass.

Active transport

OCR A	B4	✓
OCR B	B4	✓
EDEXCEL	B2	✓
WJEC	B2	✓

Sometimes substances have to be moved from a place where they are in low concentration to where they are in high concentration. This is in the opposite direction to diffusion and is called **active transport**.

You can use the phrase 'up or against the diffusion gradient' because this means in the opposite direction to diffusion. Do not say that active transport is 'along' or 'down the diffusion gradient' because this is the wrong way.

KEY POINT

Active transport is therefore the movement of a substance against the diffusion gradient with the use of energy from respiration.

Anything that stops respiration will therefore stop active transport. For example, plants take up minerals by active transport. Farmers try and make sure that their soil is not waterlogged because this reduces the oxygen content of the soil, so less oxygen is available to the root cells for respiration. This would therefore reduce the uptake of minerals.

PROGRESS CHECK

1. Why does the smell from a 'stink bomb' spread across a room?
2. Why do bad smells travel faster in warmer weather?
3. What is a partially permeable membrane?
4. What substance moves in osmosis?
5. Why does waterlogged soil have less oxygen in it?

1. The molecules move from a high concentration to a low concentration over the other side of the room.
2. Diffusion is faster in warm conditions because the molecules are moving faster.
3. A membrane that lets some molecules through but not others.
4. Water.
5. The air spaces between the soil particles have been filled with water which takes the place of oxygen.

2.7 Respiration

LEARNING SUMMARY

After studying this section you should be able to:

- describe the process of aerobic respiration and ATP production
- explain how anaerobic respiration differs from aerobic respiration
- describe how the rate of respiration can be measured.

What is energy needed for?

AQA	B2	✓
OCR A	B4	✓
OCR B	B3	✓
EDEXCEL	B2	✓
WJEC	B2	✓

The energy that is released by respiration can be used for many processes:

- To make large molecules from smaller ones, for example proteins from amino acids.
- To contract the muscles.
- For mammals and birds to keep a constant temperature.
- For active transport.

KEY POINT

Aerobic respiration is when glucose reacts with oxygen to release energy.

When you are learning the equation for respiration, look at the equation for photosynthesis in the next topic (page 46). Remember that one is just the reverse of the other. Do not try and learn them separately.

Carbon dioxide (CO_2) and water (H_2O) are released as waste products:

glucose + oxygen → carbon dioxide + water + energy

$C_6H_{12}O_6 + 6O_2 \rightarrow 6CO_2 + 6H_2O$ (+ energy released)

The reactions of aerobic respiration take place in mitochondria. All the reactions that occur in our body are called our **metabolism** and so anything that increases our **metabolic rate** will increase our respiration. During exercise the body needs more energy and so the rate of respiration increases.

The breathing rate increases to obtain extra oxygen and remove carbon dioxide from the body. The heart beats faster so that the blood can transport the oxygen, glucose and carbon dioxide faster. This is why our pulse rate increases.

ATP

OCR B   B3   ✓

The energy released by respiration is needed for different processes in different parts of the cell. To make sure that the energy is not lost as heat it is trapped in the bonds of a molecule called ATP. ATP can then pass the energy on to wherever it is needed.

Anaerobic respiration

AQA   B2   ✓
OCR A   B4   ✓
OCR B   B3   ✓
EDEXCEL   B2   ✓
WJEC   B2   ✓

KEY POINT

When not enough oxygen is available, glucose can be broken down by **anaerobic respiration**.

This may happen in muscle cells during hard exercise.

In humans: **glucose → lactic acid + (energy released)**

Being able to respire without oxygen sounds a great idea. However, there are two problems:

- Anaerobic respiration releases much less energy than is released by aerobic respiration.
- Anaerobic respiration produces lactic acid which causes muscle fatigue and pain.

In plants and fungi, such as yeast, anaerobic respiration is often called **fermentation**. It produces different products.

In plants and fungi: **glucose → ethanol + carbon dioxide + (energy released)**

KEY POINT

The build-up of lactic acid in the muscles is called the **oxygen debt** because it needs extra oxygen to be taken in after exercise to deal with it.

Another name for this is **excess post-exercise oxygen consumption (EPOC)**.

The lactic acid is transported to the liver and the heart continues to beat faster to supply the liver with the oxygen needed to break down the lactic acid.

Measuring respiration rate

OCR B   B3   ✓

It is possible to measure the respiration rate of organisms by measuring:

- the oxygen consumption
- the carbon dioxide production.

Investigating the rate of oxygen consumption.

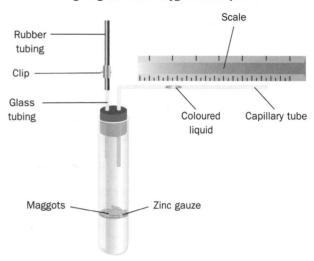

This apparatus can be used to investigate the rate of oxygen consumption by the maggots. If a liquid that absorbs carbon dioxide is placed in the bottom of the test tube then the coloured liquid will move to the left. Using this apparatus it is possible to investigate the effect of factors such as temperature or pH on the rate of respiration, e.g. by carrying out the experiment at different temperatures. It is also possible to calculate the **respiratory quotient (RQ)** using this formula:

$$RQ = \frac{\text{carbon dioxide produced}}{\text{oxygen used}}$$

The RQ provides useful information about what type of substance is being respired.

> **Remember that respiration is controlled by enzymes. This means that any factors that will change the rate of enzyme reactions will also change the rate of respiration.**

PROGRESS CHECK

1. Why do we need to eat more in cold weather?
2. Why do we breathe faster when we exercise?
3. What are the bubbles of gas given off when yeast is fermenting glucose?
4. Why do our muscles hurt when we run a long race?
5. Look at the equation for aerobic respiration using glucose. What would be the RQ of an organism that is respiring only glucose?
6. Wine makers need to control the temperature carefully inside the fermentation tanks when they make wine using fermentation. Explain why.

1. We need to respire more to generate more heat to keep a constant body temperature, so more food is needed to provide glucose for respiration to produce this heat.
2. Respiration rate increases to supply extra energy for muscle contraction. More oxygen is therefore needed and more carbon dioxide needs to be removed.
3. Carbon dioxide.
4. Lactic acid is produced due to anaerobic respiration.
5. 6/6 = 1.0
6. So that the temperature is at an optimum level for the yeast enzymes to produce alcohol.

Sample GCSE questions

1   Grace is doing an experiment to demonstrate osmosis.

She uses a special material called dialysis tubing to make a bag.

The dialysis tubing is selectively permeable.

She half fills the bag with sugar solution and measures its mass.

Grace then lowers the bag into a beaker of sugar solution.

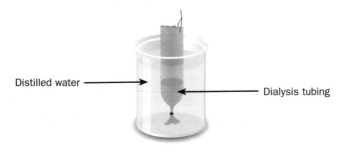

Distilled water ⟶   ⟵ Dialysis tubing

(a)   The bag is partially permeable. What is meant by partially
permeable?   [2]

*This means that some molecules can get through and not
others.*

It is important to
say that it is usually
smaller molecules
that can get through.

(b)   After thirty minutes Grace takes the bag out of the water and wipes
it with a tissue. She then reweighs it.

She repeats this experiment with different concentrations of sugar
solution in the beaker.

The solution in the bag is always the same concentration.

Her results are shown in the table.

Concentration of sugar in beaker (mol per dm^3)	Mass of bag before (g)	Mass of bag after (g)	% change in mass
0.0	4.90	5.51	12.40
0.2	4.70	5.10	8.50
0.4	4.80	4.85	1.04
0.6	4.80	4.66	
0.8	5.20	4.81	−7.50

(i)   Suggest why Grace wipes the outside of the bag with a tissue
before she reweighs it.   [1]

*This is to make sure that she is not weighing any liquid
that is on the outside of the bag.*

Sample GCSE questions

(ii) Work out the percentage change in mass for the bag in the 0.6 mol per dm³ sugar solution. **[2]**

$$4.66 - 4.80 = \frac{-0.14}{4.80} \times 100 = -2.92\%$$

> Make sure that you can do these calculations. Percentage change is the
> $$\frac{\text{difference in mass}}{\text{initial mass}} \times 100$$
> This has a minus sign because it is decreasing.

(iii) Plot the results on the grid.

Finish the graph by drawing the best straight line. **[4]**

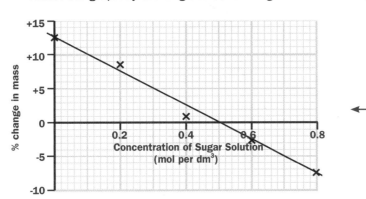

> When plotting graphs:
> • Make sure you choose a scale that uses at least half the graph paper.
> • Label the axes with units as well.
>
> Remember that a best straight line or best curve does not have to go through any of the points.

(iv) Describe what happened to the mass of the bag when it was placed into different concentrations of sugar solution. **[2]**

In weak solutions it gained in mass and in strong solutions it lost mass.

> You should really say what you mean by weak and strong solutions here. Looking at the graph weak is less than 0.5 mol per dm³ and strong is more than 0.5 mol per dm³.

(v) Explain why the mass of the bag changed in the different solutions. **[3]**

In weak solutions water passes into the bag by osmosis. This is because the contents are more concentrated.

In stronger solutions water leaves the bag because the gradient is reversed.

> This is correct but it is worth saying that the dialysis tubing is acting as a partially permeable membrane.

(vi) Use the graph to estimate the concentration of sugar solution that was in the bag. Explain how you can tell this from the graph. **[2]**

0.5 mol per dm³

This is the concentration at which no water leaves or enters the bag so the mass does not change.

> This should really say that water is entering and leaving at the same rate.

Exam practice questions

1 An athlete starts to run a race.

(a) **(i)** Aerobic respiration is taking place in his muscle cells.

Complete the balanced **symbol** equation for aerobic respiration.

$C_6H_{12}O_6$ + ... → .... + $6H_2O$ + (ENERGY RELEASED)   **[2]**

(ii) The athlete's breathing rate increases during the race.

Explain why.

....

....

.... **[3]**

(b) Towards the end of the race anaerobic respiration is taking place in the athlete's muscle cells.

Write the **word** equation for anaerobic respiration.

.... **[1]**

(c) When the athlete has finished the race his breathing rate stays high for some time.

Why does his breathing rate stay high for some time?

....

....

.... **[3]**

Exam practice questions

2 The graphs show how the rates of reaction of two different enzymes alter with temperature.

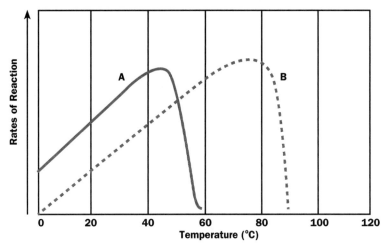

(a) Describe how the rate of reaction with enzyme A alters with temperature.

....

....

.... **[3]**

(b) Explain why the reaction rate alters with temperature.

....

....

.... **[3]**

(c) One of these enzymes is from a human.

The other is from a bacterium that lives in very hot volcanic springs.

Which enzyme is which? Use data from the graph to support your answer.

....

.... **[2]**

Exam practice questions

3 The diagram shows DNA replicating.

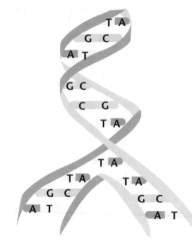

(a) Use the diagram to help you explain how DNA replicates.

....

....

.... **[3]**

(b) DNA replicates before cells divide.

Cells can divide by **mitosis** or by **meiosis**.

Finish this table to show differences between cells made by the two processes.

Feature	Mitosis	Meiosis
Number of cells made from one cell	Two	
Uses of cells that are made		Sex cells
Number of chromosomes made in the cells	Same number as the parent cells	

[3]

(c) The diagram shows a cell dividing by meiosis.

The cell is shown during the first division of meiosis and in the second division.

Describe the differences between the two diagrams.

.... **[2]**

3 Sampling organisms

The following topics are covered in this chapter:

- **Sampling techniques**
- **Food production – photosynthesis**
- **Farming techniques**

3.1 Sampling techniques

LEARNING SUMMARY

After studying this section, you should be able to:

- recall the meaning of the terms habitat, population, community and ecosystem
- describe techniques for mapping and sampling an area
- explain what is meant by zonation.

Where do organisms live?

AQA	B2	✓
OCR A	B4	✓
OCR B	B4	✓
EDEXCEL	B2	✓
WJEC	B2	✓

Different organisms live in different environments.

- The place where an organism lives is called its **habitat**.
- All the organisms of one type living in a habitat are called a **population**.
- All the populations in a habitat are a **community**.
- An **ecosystem** is all the living and non-living things in a habitat.

> Remember that for two organisms to be in the same population they must live in the same habitat and be in the same species. This means that they can successfully mate with each other.

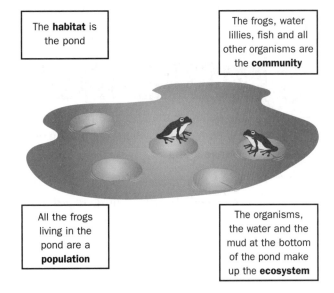

The **habitat** is the pond

The frogs, water lillies, fish and all other organisms are the **community**

All the frogs living in the pond are a **population**

The organisms, the water and the mud at the bottom of the pond make up the **ecosystem**

3 Sampling organisms

Sampling an area

AQA	B2	✓
OCR A	B4	✓
OCR B	B4	✓
EDEXCEL	B2	✓
WJEC	B2	✓

It is possible to investigate where organisms live by using various devices.

A **quadrat** is a small square that is put on the ground within which all species of interest are noted or measurements taken. The number of organisms can be counted, or the percentage cover estimated in the quadrat, and the size of the population in the whole area can then be estimated. Often several quadrats are required to determine the estimate.

Quadrats are often used to study plants, but devices such as **pooters**, **nets** and **pitfall traps** can be used to sample animal populations.

It is easy to try and estimate how many of one type of plant live in a habitat:

- Work out the area of the whole habitat.
- Sample a small area using several quadrats and count out how many plants are present.
- Scale up this number to give an estimate of the population in the whole habitat.

Working out the population of animals is harder because they do not keep still to be counted!

We can use a technique called **mark–recapture**:

- The organisms, such as snails, are captured, unharmed.
- They are counted and then marked in some way, for example the snail can be marked with a dot of non-toxic paint.
- They are released.
- Some time later the process of capturing is repeated and another count is made.
- This count includes the number of marked animals and the number unmarked.

Remember in all sampling questions, the more samples that you take in an area, the more accurate the estimate of the whole area will be.

To work out the estimate of the population a formula is used.

Population size is:

$$\frac{\text{number in 1st sample} \times \text{number in 2nd sample}}{\text{number in 2nd sample previously marked}}$$

Mapping an area

AQA	B2	✓
OCR A	B4	✓
OCR B	B4	✓
EDEXCEL	B2	✓
WJEC	B2	✓

To estimate the size of a population in an area we can use quadrats put down at random. To see where the organisms live in a habitat we can use a **transect line**:

- A tape measure is put down in a line across the habitat.
- Quadrats are put down at set intervals along the tape.
- The organisms in the quadrats are then counted.

Zonation

OCR B | B4 | ✓

In some habitats a transect line can produce interesting results. Different organisms live at different points along the line. This is because there is a change in environmental conditions along the line. This is called **zonation**.

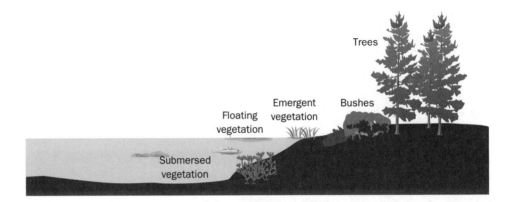

An example of zonation is found in a pond. Different plants can grow at different distances into the pond. This is due to the amount of water in the soil.

Artificial ecosystems

OCR B | B4 | ✓

Our planet has a range of different ecosystems. Some of these are **natural**, such as woodland and lakes. Others are **artificial** and have been created by man, such as fish farms, greenhouses and fields of crops.

Artificial ecosystems usually have less variety of organisms living there (less biodiversity). This may be caused by the use of chemicals such as weed killers, pesticides and fertilisers.

PROGRESS CHECK

1. What name is given to all the rabbits living in the same field?
2. What device would you use to sample **a)** daisies on a field, **b)** butterflies and **c)** woodlice?
3. Five daisy plants are found in 0.25 m². How many would there be in the whole 100 m² field?
4. Why is it best to sample several areas in the field and take an average?
5. 30 snails are collected in an area, marked and released. When another sample is captured there are 35 snails and 5 are marked. What is an estimate of the snail population?
6. Different animals live on different parts of a rocky shore on the way down to the sea. Use the idea of tides to explain why the animals show zonation.

6. Some animals can survive more time out of the water than others and so can live further up the shore.
5. 210
4. One area of the field may not be representative of all the areas.
3. 20 in 1 m² so 2000 in the field.
2. **a)** quadrat; **b)** net; **c)** pitfall trap.
1. A population.

3.2 Food production – photosynthesis

LEARNING SUMMARY	**After studying this section, you should be able to:**

- recall the word and symbol equations for photosynthesis
- describe leaf structure
- describe how the understanding of photosynthesis has developed
- explain what is meant by limiting factors.

The reactions of photosynthesis

AQA	B2	✓
OCR A	B4	✓
OCR B	B4	✓
EDEXCEL	B2	✓
WJEC	B2	✓

> **KEY POINT**
>
> Plants make their own food by a process called **photosynthesis**.

> Try this for remembering the equation for photosynthesis:
>
> **C**ertain **W**orms **E**at **G**rass **O**utside (**c**arbon dioxide **w**ater **e**nergy **g**lucose **o**xygen).

They take in carbon dioxide and water and turn it into sugar, releasing oxygen as a waste product. The process needs the energy from sunlight and this is trapped by the green pigment **chlorophyll**.

(light energy)

carbon dioxide + water → glucose + oxygen

(chlorophyll)

$$6CO_2 + 6H_2O \rightarrow C_6H_{12}O_6 + 6O_2$$

Where does photosynthesis happen?

AQA	B2	✓
OCR A	B4	✓
OCR B	B4	✓
EDEXCEL	B2	✓

Photosynthesis occurs mainly in the leaves.

Cross section of a leaf.

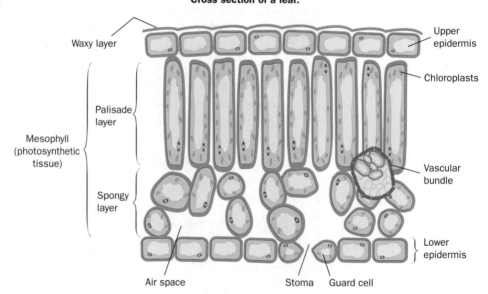

Waxy layer

Upper epidermis

Chloroplasts

Palisade layer

Mesophyll (photosynthetic tissue)

Spongy layer

Vascular bundle

Air space

Stoma   Guard cell

Lower epidermis

The leaves are specially adapted for photosynthesis in a number of ways:

Adaptation	How it helps photosynthesis
A broad shape	Provides a large surface area to absorb light and CO_2
A flat shape	The gases do not have too far to diffuse
Contains a network of veins	Supplies water from the roots and takes away the products
Contains many chloroplasts in the palisade layer near the top	This traps the maximum amount of light
Pores called stomata and air spaces	They allow gases to diffuse into the leaf and reach the cells

Photosynthesis experiments

AQA	B2	✓
OCR A	B4	✓
OCR B	B4	✓
EDEXCEL	B2	✓
WJEC	B2	✓

'How Science Works' questions may ask for examples of how ideas in science have changed over the years. The discoveries made in photosynthesis are good examples to use.

The understanding of the process of photosynthesis has changed considerably during history:

- Greek scientists thought that plants gained mass only by taking in minerals from the soil.
- Van Helmont in the seventeenth century worked out that plant growth cannot be solely due to minerals from the soil. He found that the mass gained by a plant was more than the mass lost by the soil.
- In the eighteenth century Priestley showed that oxygen is produced by plants.

More modern experiments using **isotopes** have increased our understanding of photosynthesis. Isotopes of carbon can be used that behave in the same way chemically, but can be followed in the reactions because they are radioactive.

These experiments have shown that photosynthesis is a two stage process:

- Light energy is used to split water, releasing oxygen gas and hydrogen atoms.
- Carbon dioxide gas combines with the hydrogen to make glucose and water.

The rate of photosynthesis can be increased by providing:

- more light
- more carbon dioxide
- an optimum temperature.

Any of these factors can be **limiting factors**.

> **KEY POINT**
>
> A limiting factor is something that controls how fast a reaction will occur.

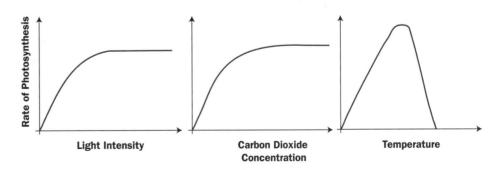

Many candidates think that plants respire at night and photosynthesise during the day. To get an A* you must realise that plants carry out respiration all the time. Fortunately for us, during the day, they photosynthesise much faster than they respire, so overall they release more oxygen than they take in.

If more light is provided, it will increase photosynthesis because more energy is available.

After a certain point something else will limit the rate.

More carbon dioxide will again increase the rate up to a point because more raw materials are present.

Increasing the temperature will make enzymes work faster, but high temperatures denature enzymes.

PROGRESS CHECK

1. What is the job of chlorophyll in photosynthesis?
2. Which cells in the leaf have most chloroplasts?
3. What are stomata?
4. Why do leaves have veins?
5. In the reactions of photosynthesis is oxygen released from water, carbon dioxide or both?
6. Why do high temperatures stop photosynthesis happening?

6. High temperatures will denature the enzymes that control the reactions of photosynthesis.
5. It is released from water.
4. To supply water for photosynthesis and to take away the sugars that are produced from photosynthesis.
3. Structures containing leaf pores that allow gases in and out of the leaf.
2. Palisade mesophyll.
1. To absorb the energy of sunlight.

3.3 Farming techniques

LEARNING SUMMARY

After studying this section, you should be able to:

- describe the uses that plants have for glucose
- describe methods for intensive food production
- explain how intensive food production increases yields
- describe how organic farming differs from intensive farming
- describe the main methods for food preservation.

Plants need minerals

AQA	B2	✓
OCR A	B4	✓
OCR B	B4	✓
WJEC	B2	✓

Once plants have made sugars, such as glucose by photosynthesis, they can convert the glucose into many different things that they need to grow:

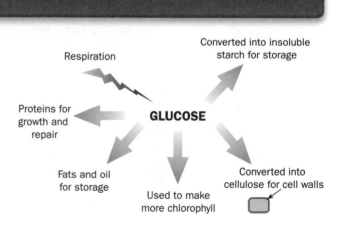

To produce these chemicals, plants need various minerals from the soil:

- **Nitrates** as a supply of nitrogen to make amino acids and proteins.
- **Phosphates** to supply phosphorus to make DNA and cell membranes.
- **Potassium** to help enzymes in respiration and photosynthesis.
- **Magnesium** to make chlorophyll.

Without these minerals plants do not grow properly. So farmers must make sure that they are available in the soil.

> Fertilisers are labelled with figures called an NPK value. This gives the ratio of nitrates, phosphates and potassium in the fertiliser.

Intensive food production

OCR B   B4   ✓

The human population is increasing and so there is a greater demand for food. This means that many farmers now use **intensive farming** methods.

> **KEY POINT**
>
> Intensive farming means trying to obtain as much food as possible from the land.

There are a number of different food production systems that use intensive methods:

Fish farming

Fish are kept in enclosures away from predators. Their food supply and pests are controlled.

Glasshouses

Plants can be grown in areas where the climate would not be suitable. They can also produce crops at different times of the year.

Hydroponics

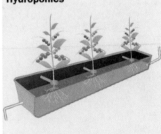

Plants are grown without soil. They need extra support but their mineral supply and pests are controlled.

Energy flow in food production

OCR B   B4   ✓

Farmers use a number of intensive farming techniques to help increase their yield:

> 'How Science Works' questions may ask for the arguments for and against methods of intensive farming. Make sure that you can give both sides of the argument.

Using pesticides to kill pests that might eat the crop

Using herbicides to kill weeds that would compete with the crop

INTENSIVE FARMING

Keep animals indoors so that they do not waste energy keeping warm or moving about

Provide the plants with chemical fertilisers for growth

One argument is that the damage caused by some of these techniques does not justify the increase in food production.

Organic food production

| OCR B | B4 | ✓ |
| WJEC | B2 | ✓ |

Many people think that intensive farming is harmful to the environment and cruel to animals.

> **KEY POINT**
>
> Farming that does not use the intensive methods is called **organic farming**.

Organic farming uses a number of different techniques:

Technique	Details
Use of manure and compost	These provide minerals for the plant instead of using chemical fertilisers.
Crop rotation	Farmers do not grow the same crop in the same field year after year. This stops the build-up of pests and often reduces nutrient depletion of the soil.
Use of nitrogen fixing crops	These crops contain bacteria that add minerals to the soil.
Weeding	This means that chemical herbicides are not needed.
Varying planting times	This can help to avoid times that pests are active.
Using biological control	Farmers can use living organisms to help to control pests. They may eat them or cause disease.

Preserving food

| OCR B | B4 | ✓ |

Although gardeners want decay to happen in their compost heaps, people do not want their food to decay before they can eat it.

> **KEY POINT**
>
> **Food preservation** methods reduce the rate of decay of foods.

There are many ways to preserve food. Most stop decay by taking away one of the factors that decomposers need:

Preservation method	How it is done	How does it work?
Canning	Food is heated in a can and the can is sealed.	The high temperature kills the microorganisms and oxygen cannot get into the can after it is sealed.
Cooling	Food is kept in a refrigerator at about 5°C.	The growth and respiration of the decomposers slow down at low temperature.
Freezing	Food is kept in a freezer at about −18°C.	The decomposers cannot respire or reproduce.
Drying	Dry air is passed over the food.	Microorganisms cannot respire or reproduce without water.
Adding salt or sugar	Food is soaked in a sugar solution or packed in salt.	The sugar or salt draws water out of the decomposers.
Adding vinegar	The food is soaked in vinegar.	The vinegar is too acidic for the decomposers.

> **Make sure that you can explain how a food preservation method stops decay.**

Modern methods of food packaging can help to increase the shelf life of food and to detect contaminants. Some of these methods involve the use of **nanotechnology**. For example, nanosensors in plastic packaging can detect gases given off by food when it spoils and the packaging changes colour as an alert that the food has gone bad.

PROGRESS CHECK

1. Why do plants need nitrates?
2. Why does a plant look yellow if grown with a lack of magnesium?
3. What is hydroponics?
4. Why does food still go bad in a refrigerator?
5. Suggest one problem with using large quantities of chemical pesticides to kill insect pests.
6. Why is the food brought to pigs in intensive farming rather than letting them find food?

1. To produce amino acids and therefore proteins.
2. Chlorophyll cannot be made as chlorophyll contains magnesium.
3. Growing plants without the use of soil, just in water.
4. The temperature is not low enough to completely stop the growth of microbes that cause decay.
5. Often they kill the natural predators of the pests too and so increase the problem. They also contaminate the environment and reduce biodiversity.
6. It prevents loss of energy in pig movement therefore leaving more energy for growth.

Sample GCSE questions

1 **(a)** Plants absorb energy from sunlight to make food by photosynthesis.

Complete the balanced symbol equation for photosynthesis. **[2]**

(light energy)

$$6CO_2 + 6H_2O \rightarrow C_6H_{12}O_6 + 6O_2$$

(chlorophyll)

> Make sure that you follow the same rules as for chemistry equations and use the correct size numbers and letters.

(b) The chloroplasts that absorb light energy for photosynthesis are found mainly near the top surface of the leaf.

Stomata that absorb carbon dioxide are found on the lower surface.

Explain these two observations. **[3]**

The chloroplasts are towards the top of the leaf because that is where the light energy is at its greatest.

Stomata, however, are on the underside to try and reduce water loss. It is cooler and there is less air movement underneath the leaf so less water is lost.

> A good answer. You could use the term transpiration to describe the loss of water.

(c) Plants only photosynthesise during the day but respire all the time.

How can plants manage to make more glucose than they use? **[2]**

During the daytime the rate of photosynthesis is usually much greater than the rate of respiration.

At night only respiration occurs but the sugar used up is less than the surplus made during the day.

> Remember that plants respire day and night. Many candidates think that they only respire at night.

(d) The graph shows the rate of photosynthesis as light intensity changes at three different concentrations of carbon dioxide.

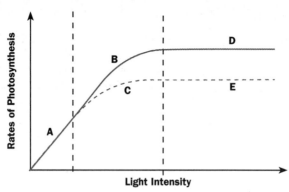

Which letter (**A**, **B**, **C**, **D** or **E**) shows where carbon dioxide is the only limiting factor? Explain your answer. **[3]**

E. It is the only section of the graph where increasing the concentration of carbon dioxide increases the rate but increasing light intensity does not.

> Limiting factors is a difficult idea. Remember that a factor is limiting if increasing that factor will increase the rate of photosynthesis.

Exam practice questions

1   Kane investigates a pond.

He observes various plants and animals that live in the pond.

(a)   Using the area that Kane investigated, explain what is meant by the following terms.

(i)   habitat

....

.... **[1]**

(ii)   population

....

.... **[1]**

(iii)   ecosystem

....

.... **[1]**

(b)   Kane wants to work out how many snails there are in the pond.

He decides to sample one small area of 1 m^2.

In this area he catches five snails.

(i)   What device might he use to catch the snails?

.... **[1]**

(ii)   Kane measures the diameter of the circular pond as 15 metres.

Work out an estimate of the number of snails in the whole pond.

answer = ... snails   **[2]**

(iii)   Kane then tries another method.

He samples in five different areas, catches and marks 30 snails.

He releases them and then samples in the same way the next day.

He catches 29 snails and two were marked.

Use this formula to estimate the number of snails in the pond:

$$\text{number of snails} = \frac{\text{number in first sample} \times \text{number in second sample}}{\text{number in the second sample that have been marked}}$$

answer = ... snails   **[2]**

(iv)   Which of Kane's two estimates is likely to be the most accurate?

Explain why.

....

.... **[2]**

Exam practice questions

2 In the seventeenth century a Dutch scientist called van Helmont carried out a famous experiment.

At that time people thought that plants obtained their food from the soil.

He grew a tree in a pot of soil, supplying it only with rain water.

The diagram shows the measurements that he took.

| 2 kg tree | + | 100 kg soil | Tree grows for 5 years with rain water | 80 kg tree | + | 99 kg soil |

(a) **(i)** Explain how van Helmont used these results to disprove the idea that plants gain their food entirely from the soil.

....

....

.... **[2]**

(ii) Van Helmont concluded that the tree gained in mass entirely from the rain water.

To what extent is this true?

....

....

.... **[3]**

(b) In 1953 an American scientist called Melvin Calvin worked out many of the reactions of photosynthesis.

How would he communicate his ideas to other scientists and how would these methods differ from those used by van Helmont?

....

....

....

.... **[3]**

Exam practice questions

3 Red spiders are pests of plants that grow in greenhouses such as tomatoes.

(a) The spiders can be killed by spraying with an insecticide.

(i) Some gardeners do not want to spray their tomato plants with insecticide.

Suggest a reason why.

....

.... **[1]**

(ii) Over a number of years an insecticide may become less effective in killing the spiders.

Suggest why this might be.

.... **[1]**

(b) Another way to kill the spiders is to buy some mites.

The mites can be released into the greenhouse to eat the spiders.

(i) The use of the mite is an example of a different type of pest control.

What is it called?

.... **[1]**

(ii) Scientists have to be careful when they introduce this type of control.

Explain why.

....

.... **[2]**

(c) Some farmers grow tomatoes with their roots in liquid rather than in soil.

What name is given to this method of growing crops and what are the advantages?

....

....

....

.... **[3]**

4 Physiology

The following topics are covered in this chapter:

- **Transport in animals**
- **Transport in plants**
- **Digestion and absorption**

4.1 Transport in animals

LEARNING SUMMARY

After studying this section, you should be able to:

- describe the roles of the different cells found in blood
- compare the structure and function of the different types of blood vessels
- describe the structure of the heart and the double circulation.

Blood

| OCR B | B3 | ✓ |
| EDEXCEL | B2 | ✓ |

Blood is made up of a liquid called **plasma**.

> **KEY POINT**
>
> Plasma carries chemicals such as dissolved food, hormones, antibodies and waste products around the body.

Cells are also carried in the plasma. They are adapted for different jobs.

Red blood cells are shaped like a biconcave disc. They contain haemoglobin which can carry oxygen around the body.

A red blood cell.

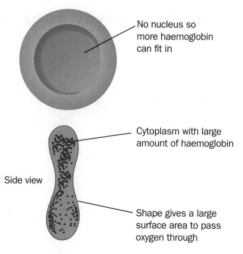

No nucleus so more haemoglobin can fit in

Cytoplasm with large amount of haemoglobin

Side view

Shape gives a large surface area to pass oxygen through

> The shape of red blood cells does not allow them to carry more oxygen, but the increased surface area to volume ratio lets them gain or lose it quicker.

The haemoglobin in red blood cells reacts with oxygen in the lungs forming **oxyhaemoglobin**.

In the tissues the reverse of this reaction happens and oxygen is released:

haemoglobin + oxygen ⇌ oxyhaemoglobin

KEY POINT

White blood cells can change shape to engulf and destroy disease organisms. They can also produce antibodies.

Platelets are responsible for clotting the blood.

The blood is carried around the body in **arteries**, **veins** and **capillaries**.

Arteries	Veins	Capillaries
Carry blood away from the heart	Carry blood back to the heart	Join arteries to veins.
Have thick, muscular walls because the blood is under high pressure	Have valves and a wide lumen because the blood is under low pressure.	Have permeable walls so that substances can pass in and out to the tissues.

You need to remember Arteries carry blood <u>a</u>way from the heart and ve<u>IN</u>s back <u>IN</u>to the heart.

The heart

OCR B   B3 ✓
EDEXCEL B2 ✓

KEY POINT

The heart is made up of four chambers.

The top two chambers are called **atria** and they receive blood from veins. The bottom two chambers are **ventricles**. They pump the blood out into arteries.

The top two chambers, the atria, fill up with blood returning in the **vena cava** and **pulmonary veins**. The two atria then contract together and pump the blood down into the ventricles. The two ventricles then contract pumping blood out into the **aorta** and **pulmonary artery** at high pressure.

Make sure that you can spot that the muscle wall of the left ventricle is always thicker than the right ventricle. This is because it has to pump blood all round the body compared to the short distance to the lungs.

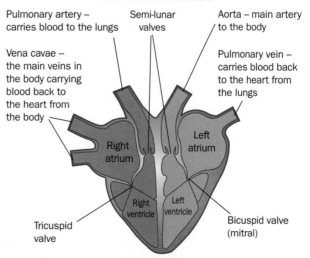

Cross section of a heart.

KEY POINT

In the heart there are two sets of valves, whose function is to prevent blood flowing backwards.

In between the atria and the ventricles are the **bicuspid** and **tricuspid valves**. These valves stop blood flowing back into the atria when the ventricles contract. The pressure of blood closes the flaps of the valves and the tendons stop the flaps turning inside out. There are also **semi-lunar** valves between the ventricles and the arteries.

A double circulation

OCR B B3 ✓

KEY POINT

Mammals have a **double circulation**. This means that the blood has to pass through the heart twice on each circuit of the body.

Deoxygenated blood is pumped to the lungs and the oxygenated blood returns to the heart to be pumped to the body.

The advantage of this system is that the pressure of the blood stays quite high and so it can flow faster around the body. Because of the double circulation the heart is really two pumps in one:

- The right side pumps the blood to the lungs.
- The left side pumps it to the rest of the body.

PROGRESS CHECK

1. What is the job of platelets?
2. Why do red blood cells lack a nucleus?
3. Why do veins have valves?
4. What blood vessel carries blood from the heart to the lungs?
5. Why is the right side of the heart coloured blue in the diagram?
6. Some people have a defect in the bicuspid valve. Explain why this can lead to a build up of blood in the blood vessels of the lungs.

1. To clot the blood.
2. To fit more haemoglobin in and so carry more oxygen.
3. To stop the blood flowing backwards as the pressure is low.
4. Pulmonary artery.
5. It contains deoxygenated blood (which is dark red, not blue).
6. When the left ventricle contracts some of the blood goes back into the left atrium rather than out into the aorta. This causes a backlog of blood in the veins coming back from the lungs.

4.2 Transport in plants

LEARNING SUMMARY

After studying this section, you should be able to:

- describe the position and function of xylem and phloem
- explain how water moves through a plant
- explain the factors that affect transpiration rate and how it can be reduced.

Xylem and phloem

OCR B   B4   ✓
EDEXCEL B2   ✓

> **KEY POINT**
>
> Plants have two different tissues that are used to transport substances. They are called **xylem** and **phloem**.

Xylem vessels and phloem tubes are gathered together into collections called **vascular bundles**. They are found in different regions of the leaf, stem and root.

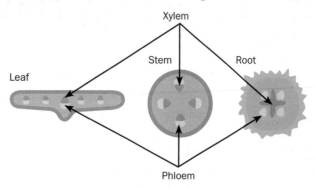

Xylem vessels and phloem tubes are different in structure and do different jobs:

Xylem	Phloem
Carries water and minerals from roots to the leaves	Carries dissolved food substances both up and down the plant
The movement of water up the plant and out of the leaves is called **transpiration**	The movement of the dissolved food is called **translocation**
Made of vessels which are hollow tubes made of thickened dead cells	Made of columns of living cells

> Remember phloem for food and xylem for water.

The movement of water

OCR B   B4   ✓
EDEXCEL B2   ✓

> **KEY POINT**
>
> Water enters the plant through the **root hairs**, by **osmosis**.

The root hair cells increase the surface area for the absorption of water.

Remember that it is osmosis that brings the water into the leaf and into the xylem, but water does not move up the xylem by osmosis. It is 'sucked up' by evaporation from the leaves.

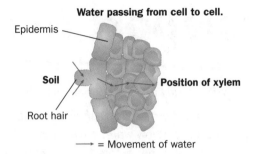

Water passing from cell to cell.

Epidermis

Soil

Root hair

Position of xylem

⟶ = Movement of water

Water then passes from cell to cell by osmosis until it reaches the centre of the root. The water enters xylem vessels in the root and then travels up the stem. Water enters the leaves and evaporates. It then passes through the **stomata** by **diffusion**.

> **KEY POINT**
>
> This loss of water is called **transpiration** and it helps to pull water up the xylem vessels.

Various environmental conditions can affect the transpiration rate.

Transpiration rate

OCR B   B4   ✓

The rate of transpiration depends on a number of factors:

- **Temperature** – warm weather increases the kinetic energy of the water molecules so they move out of the leaf faster.
- **Humidity** – damp air reduces the concentration gradient so the water molecules leave the leaf more slowly.
- **Wind** – the wind blows away the water molecules so that a large diffusion gradient is maintained.
- **Light** – light causes the stomata to open and so more water is lost.

If a question asks *Give one factor that increases transpiration rate*, make sure that you write 'an increase in temperature' not just 'temperature'. Many candidates lose marks in this way.

Adaptations to reduce water loss

OCR B   B4   ✓

When plants are short of water, they do not want to waste it through transpiration. The trouble is they need to let carbon dioxide in, so water will always be able to get out. Water loss is kept as low as possible in several ways:

- Photosynthesis only occurs during the day, so the stomata close at night to reduce water loss. The guard cells lose water by osmosis and become flaccid. This closes the stoma.
- The stomata are on the underside of the leaf. This reduces water loss because they are away from direct sunlight and protected from the wind.
- The top surface of the leaf, facing the Sun, is often covered with a protective waxy layer.

Although transpiration is kept as low as possible, it does help plants by cooling them down and supplying leaves with minerals. It also provides water for support and photosynthesis.

PROGRESS CHECK

PROGRESS CHECK

1. In which direction in a plant stem does water and minerals move?
2. What is translocation?
3. Where in a plant root is xylem found?
4. What is the function of root hair cells?
5. Why is it impossible for plants to prevent all water loss from the leaves?
6. What causes stomata to close when a plant wilts?

6. The guard cells lose water by osmosis and so the cells become flaccid, straightening up and closing the pore.
5. Because carbon dioxide must be allowed in for photosynthesis.
4. To increase the surface area for water absorption.
3. In the centre, in a star shape.
2. The movement of dissolved food through the phloem.
1. Up, towards the leaves.

4.3 Digestion and absorption

LEARNING SUMMARY

After studying this section, you should be able to:

- describe the position and function of the main parts of the digestive system
- describe how the products of digestion are absorbed
- describe some other uses of digestive enzymes.

Digestion

AQA	B2	✓
EDEXCEL	B2	✓
WJEC	B2	✓

KEY POINT

The job of the digestive system is to break down large food molecules into small soluble molecules. This is called **digestion**.

Digestion happens in two main ways – **physical** and **chemical** digestion.

Physical digestion occurs in the mouth where the teeth break up the food into smaller pieces. Chemical digestion is caused by digestive enzymes that are released at various points along the digestive system. Most enzymes work inside cells controlling reactions. Some enzymes pass out of cells and work in the digestive system. These enzymes digest our food, making the molecules small enough to be absorbed.

The digestive system.

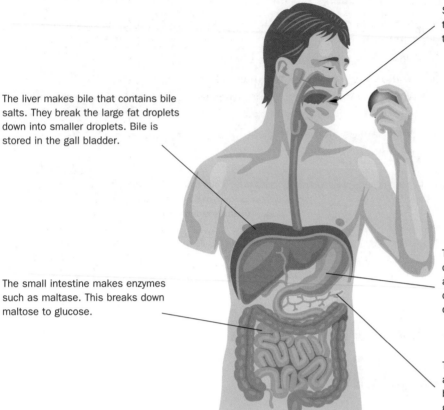

Saliva is released into the mouth from the salivary glands. It contains amylase to break down starch to maltose.

The liver makes bile that contains bile salts. They break the large fat droplets down into smaller droplets. Bile is stored in the gall bladder.

The stomach makes gastric juice, containing protease and hydrochloric acid. The acid kills microbes and creates the best pH for the protease to digest proteins.

The small intestine makes enzymes such as maltase. This breaks down maltose to glucose.

The pancreas makes more protease and amylase. It also makes lipase to break down the fats to fatty acids and glycerol.

The food is moved along the gut by contractions of the muscle in the lining of the intestine. This process is called **peristalsis**.

The rate of digestion

EDEXCEL B2 ✓
WJEC B2 ✓

To make the digestive enzymes work at an optimum rate the digestive system provides the best conditions:

Be careful not to say that bile salts break down fats. Make sure that you say 'fat droplets' otherwise it sound like bile salts are doing the same job as lipase.

- Each enzyme has a different optimum pH. Protease in the stomach works best at about pH 2, but a different protease made by the pancreas works best at about pH 9.
- Physical digestion helps to break the food into smaller particles, thereby increasing the surface area of the food particles. Bile salts **emulsify** fat droplets, breaking them into smaller droplets so lipase can work faster.

Absorption

EDEXCEL B2 ✓
WJEC B2 ✓

KEY POINT

In the small intestine small digested food molecules are absorbed into the bloodstream by diffusion.

The inside of the small intestine is permeable and has a large surface area over which absorption can take place.

The lining of the small intestine contains two types of vessels that absorb the products of digestion:

- **Capillaries** absorb food and take it to the liver via the **hepatic portal vein**.
- **Lacteals** absorb mainly the products of fat digestion and empty them into the bloodstream.

A number of factors increase the surface area of the small intestine and so speed up the rate of absorption:

- The human small intestine is over five metres long.
- The inner lining is folded.
- The folds are covered with finger-like projections called **villi**.
- The villi are further covered by smaller projections called **microvilli**.

Other uses of digestive enzymes

AQA   B2   ✓

Microorganisms also make digestive enzymes. Decay organisms such as certain bacteria and fungi release these enzymes onto the food and take up the soluble products. These organisms are called **saprophytes** (saprotrophs).

Scientists have used microorganisms such as these to supply enzymes for a number of uses:

- Biological washing powders contain proteases and lipases.
- Proteases are used to pre-digest protein in some baby foods.
- **Amylases** are used to convert starch into sugar syrup.
- **Isomerase** is used to convert glucose into fructose, which is sweeter.

Microorganisms are also used to try and improve the health of the digestive system. **Probiotics** contain live bacteria that may produce useful vitamins and neutralise toxins. Prebiotics contain food substances that are said to encourage the growth of the 'good' bacteria.

PROGRESS CHECK

1. Why does bread start to taste sweet if it is chewed for several minutes?
2. What is the function of the gall bladder?
3. What are the products of fat digestion?
4. Why is fructose used in sweets rather than glucose?
5. The lining of the stomach is protected by mucus. Why does it need to be protected?
6. People who have coeliac disease may have many of their villi destroyed. What effect might this have on the process of absorption? Explain your answer.

6. Slows down the rate of absorption as there is a smaller surface area.
5. So that the acid does not damage it and the protease does not digest it.
4. It is sweeter so less is needed.
3. Fatty acids and glycerol.
2. To store bile.
1. The starch is being digested into the sugar maltose by amylase.

Sample GCSE questions

1 **(a)** The diagram shows an external view of the human heart shown from the front.

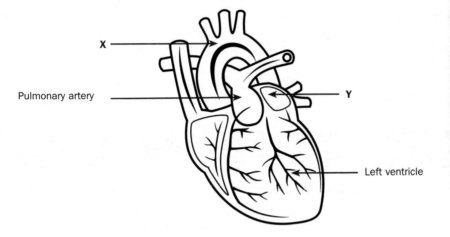

(i) Identify structures X and Y on the diagram. **[2]**

X = aorta

Y = left atrium

(ii) The pulmonary artery is labelled on the diagram.

It splits into two arteries. Why is this? **[1]**

The pulmonary artery has to carry blood to each lung.

(iii) Write down **two** differences in the composition of the blood found in the pulmonary artery and structure **X**. **[2]**

The blood in the pulmonary artery has less oxygen and more carbon dioxide.

(b) The heart has four chambers.

Explain why the walls of some of these chambers have different thicknesses.

The two atria have very thin walls because they only need to pump the blood down into the ventricles, which is not very far.

The right ventricle is thicker because it needs to pump blood to the lungs.

The left ventricle is the thickest because it needs to pump blood all around the body.

It is unusual to see a view of the outside of the heart. Most diagrams are sections of the heart which makes it easier. The two labels that are given should help you to label X and Y.

You could use the terms oxygenated or deoxygenated to describe how much oxygen is present in the blood.

This is a good answer but you should really include an explanation that the wall of the chambers contains muscle which generates pressure in the blood.

Sample GCSE questions

(c) The diagram shows a fish heart.

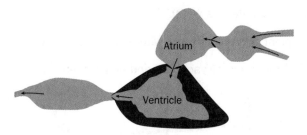

Fish only have a single circulation, not a double circulation.

Explain how you can tell this from this diagram. **[2]**

It only has one ventricle and one atrium.

This is because it does not have to pump blood to two different places.

Having a double circulation also means that deoxygenated blood and oxygenated blood needs to be kept separate in the heart.

2 **(a)** The diagram shows a section through a human blood vessel with some red blood cells inside.

(i) What type of blood cell (artery, capillary or vein) is shown in the diagram? **[1]**

A capillary

(ii) Describe how the function of this blood vessel is related to its structure. **[2]**

The job of capillaries is to allow substances to pass between the blood and the tissues.

The wall of capillaries is very thin so substances can move in and out.

The answer is correct but as well as saying that the wall is thin you should also say that it is only one cell thick.

(b) Describe **two** ways in which the shape or the structure of a red blood cell allows it to do its job efficiently. **[4]**

It is shaped like a biconcave disc. This gives it a large surface area compared to its volume so that oxygen can diffuse in and out quickly.

It also lacks a nucleus so that more haemoglobin can fit in to carry more oxygen.

Red blood cells are also small and flexible so that they can squeeze through the smallest capillaries.

Exam practice questions

1 Rosie notices that if leaves are removed from a plant they dry out and shrivel.

She designs an experiment to investigate this water loss.

She picks three leaves from a plant and paints them with nail varnish as shown in the diagram.

Rosie then accurately measures the mass of each leaf and hangs them from a piece of string.

Nail varnish on top surface

Nail varnish on bottom surface

No nail varnish

Rosie reweighs the leaves at regular intervals.

Her results are shown on the graph.

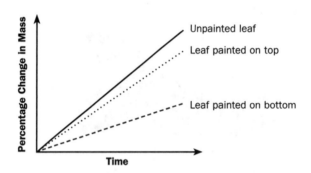

Percentage Change in Mass

Time

Unpainted leaf

Leaf painted on top

Leaf painted on bottom

(a) Describe what happens to the mass of the leaf with no nail varnish and explain the changes.

....

.... **[2]**

(b) Explain why the other two leaves change mass at different rates.

....

....

.... **[3]**

(c) The results of Rosie's experiment would have been different if she pointed a fan at the leaves. Explain why.

....

.... **[2]**

Exam practice questions

2 Until 1628, people thought that the blood was pumped by the heart.

They thought that the blood carried oxygen to the tissues and the blood then passed back to the heart in the same vessels.

(a) Explain what was correct and what was incorrect with these ideas.

....

....

.... **[3]**

(b) In 1628 William Harvey published the results of a series of experiments.

He tied a cord around the top of his arm.

He found that the veins below the cord became swollen with blood. Explain why this is.

....

.... **[1]**

(c) Harvey then emptied the blood from part of the vein by rubbing his finger back in the direction O to H in this diagram.

He found that the blood was stopped from moving backwards by small structures in the vein.

(i) What is the name of these small structures?

.... **[1]**

(ii) Why are these small structures needed in veins but not in arteries?

....

.... **[1]**

Exam practice questions

(d) Harvey predicted that there must be small vessels joining arteries to veins but he could not see them.

What is the name of these vessels and suggest why Harvey could not see them.

....

....

.... **[2]**

3 The diagram shows the human digestive system.

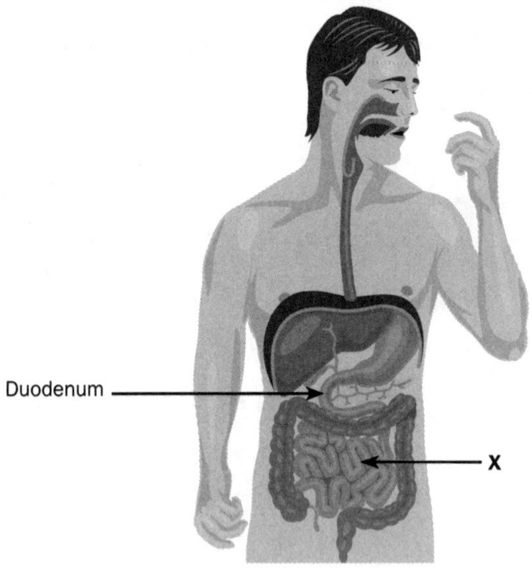

Duodenum

X

(a) **(i)** Write down the main function of the region labelled **X**.

.... **[1]**

(ii) Write down **two** ways in which the structure of **X** is adapted for this function.

1
....

2
.... **[2]**

(b) One of the liquids added to the duodenum is bile.

Explain the functions of bile.

The quality of written communication will be assessed in your answer to this question.

....

....

.... **[4]**

5 Atoms and materials

The following topics are covered in this chapter:

- Atomic structure
- Atoms and the periodic table
- Chemical reactions and atoms
- The periodic table
- Balancing equations
- Ionic and covalent bonding
- Ionic and covalent structures
- Group 7
- Nanoparticles
- Synthesis

5.1 Atomic structure

LEARNING SUMMARY

After studying this section, you should be able to:

- Name the three types of particle present in an atom.
- Describe the three types of particle in terms of mass, charge and where found.
- Use the atomic number and mass number to work out how many of each type of particle is present.
- Work out the electron arrangement for an atom of a given element.
- Describe the difference between isotopes of the same element.

Elements

OCR A	C4	✓
EDEXCEL	C2	✓
WJEC	C2	✓

KEY POINT

A substance that is made of only one type of **atom** is called an **element**.

Elements cannot be broken down chemically. Atoms of different elements have different properties. About 100 different elements have been discovered. The elements can be represented by **symbols**.

Approximately 80% of the elements are **metals**. Metals are found on the left-hand side and in the centre of the periodic table. The **non-metal** elements are found on the right-hand side of the periodic table. Elements with **intermediate properties** such as germanium are found in group 4.

Structure of the atom

AQA	C2	✓
OCR A	C4	✓
OCR B	C4	✓
EDEXCEL	C2	✓
WJEC	C2	✓

An atom has a very small, central **nucleus** that is surrounded by shells of **electrons**. The nucleus is found at the centre of the atom. It contains **protons** and **neutrons**.

- Protons have a mass of 1 **atomic mass unit (amu)** and a charge of 1+.
- Neutrons also have a mass of 1 amu but no charge.
- Electrons have a negligible mass and a charge of 1–.

Structure of an atom

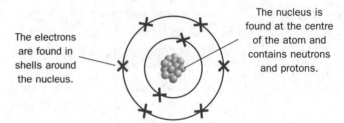

The electrons are found in shells around the nucleus.

The nucleus is found at the centre of the atom and contains neutrons and protons.

> Atoms are very small. They have a radius of about 10^{-10} m and a mass of about 10^{-23} g.

All atoms are **neutral**: there is no overall charge, so the number of protons must be equal to the number of electrons.

You may have seen two numbers written next to an element's symbol. These numbers are the **mass number** and the **atomic number**. They provide information about the particles inside the atom.

Mass number and atomic number

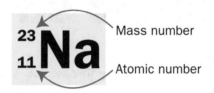

$$^{23}_{11}\text{Na}$$

Mass number

Atomic number

> Be familiar with the mass and charge of the three types of particle found inside an atom. All atoms of the same element have the same number of protons and electrons. For example, all atoms of oxygen contain 8 protons and 8 electrons.

The mass number is the number of protons added to the number of neutrons. The atomic number is the number of protons (so it is also known as the **proton number**). All the atoms of a particular element have the same number of protons, for example, carbon atoms always have six protons. Atoms of different elements have different atomic numbers.

Sodium has an atomic number of 11, so every sodium atom has 11 protons. A sodium atom has no overall charge, so the number of electrons must be the same as the number of protons. Sodium atoms therefore have 11 electrons. The number of neutrons is given by the mass number minus the atomic number. In sodium that is 23 – 11 = 12 neutrons.

Electron structure

OCR A	C4	✓
OCR B	C4	✓
EDEXCEL	C2	✓
WJEC	C2	✓

Electrons occupy the lowest available **shell** (or energy level). This is the shell that is closest to the nucleus. When this is full the electrons start to fill the next shell. In the diagram, the first shell may contain up to two electrons while the second and third shells may contain up to eight electrons.

A model of electron shells

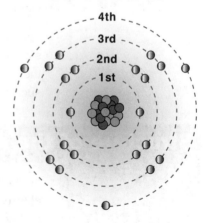

4th
3rd
2nd
1st

KEY POINT

The electron structure of an atom is important because it determines how the atom (and, therefore, the element) will react.

Groups

OCR A	C4	✓
OCR B	C4	✓
EDEXCEL	C2	✓
WJEC	C2	✓

KEY POINT

Elements in the same **group** (the same vertical column) of the periodic table have similar chemical properties because they have the same number of electrons in their outer shells.

Element	Number of protons	Number of electrons	Electronic structure	Number of shells of electrons	Group of periodic table	Period of periodic table	Diagram
Lithium	3	3	2, 1	2	1	2	
Magnesium	12	12	2, 8, 2	3	2	3	

Across a **period** (the same horizontal row in the periodic table), each consecutive element has one extra proton in its nucleus and one extra electron in its outer shell of electrons. This means an electron shell is filled with electrons across a period.

Isotopes

AQA	C2	✓
OCR B	C4	✓
EDEXCEL	C2	✓
WJEC	C2	✓

Isotopes of an element have the same number of protons but a different number of neutrons. So, they have the same **atomic number** (that is, number of protons) but a different **mass number** (that is, number of protons and neutrons added together).

Chlorine has two isotopes:

Isotope	Protons	Electrons	Neutrons	Diagram
Chlorine–35	17	17	18	$^{35}_{17}\text{Cl}$
Chlorine–37	17	17	20	$^{37}_{17}\text{Cl}$

These isotopes will have slightly different physical properties but will **react identically** in chemical reactions because they have identical numbers of electrons.

> Learn the definition for relative atomic mass.

The relative atomic mass of an element compares the mass of atoms of the element with the carbon-12 isotope. The existence of isotopes means that some elements have relative atomic masses that are not a whole number, for example, chlorine has a relative atomic mass of 35.5.

25% of chlorine atoms have an atomic mass of 37.

75% of chlorine atoms have an atomic mass of 35.

This gives an average atomic mass of 35.5.

PROGRESS CHECK

1. What does the nucleus of an atom contain?
2. Which particles are found in shells around the nucleus?
3. What is the charge and mass of a proton?
4. What is the charge and mass of an electron?
5. What is the charge and mass of a neutron?
6. What is the mass number of an atom?
7. Calcium and magnesium both belong to group 2 of the periodic table. Why does the element calcium react in a similar way to the element magnesium?

1. Protons and neutrons.
2. Electrons.
3. Charge +1, mass 1 amu.
4. Charge −1, mass negligible.
5. No charge, mass 1 amu.
6. The number of protons plus the number of neutrons.
7. As both elements are in group 2 of the periodic table they have a similar electron configuration; they both have two electrons in their outer shell.

5.2 Atoms and the periodic table

LEARNING SUMMARY

After studying this section, you should be able to:

- Describe how our understanding of atoms has changed, over time.
- Link the names of scientists to important theories about atoms.
- Describe the experiment that led Rutherford to propose the existence of a dense nucleus.
- Describe the arrangement of elements on the modern periodic table as being according to atomic number.
- Relate the group and period number of a given element to its electron arrangement.

The history of the atom

OCR A	C4	✓
OCR B	C4	✓
WJEC	C2	✓

Ideas about atoms have changed over time as more evidence has become available. Scientists look at the evidence that is available and use this to build a model of what they think is happening. As new evidence emerges they re-evaluate the model. If the model fits with the new evidence they keep it. If the model no longer works they change it.

Important advances

OCR A	C4	✓
OCR B	C4	✓
WJEC	C2	✓

John Dalton

In the early 1800s, John Dalton developed a theory about atoms, which included these predictions:

- Elements are made up of small particles called atoms.
- Atoms cannot be divided into simpler substances.
- All atoms of the same element are the same.
- Atoms of each element are different from atoms of other elements.

JJ Thomson

Between 1897 and 1906 Thomson discovered that atoms could be split into smaller particles. He discovered electrons and found that they:

- have a negative charge
- are very small
- are deflected by magnetic and electric fields.

He thought that atoms consisted of tiny negative electrons surrounded by a 'sea' of positive charge. Overall, the atom was neutral. This was called the **plum-pudding** theory of atoms.

JJ Thomson's 'plum-pudding' model of the atom

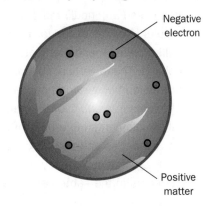

Negative electron

Positive matter

Ernest Rutherford

In 1909, Rutherford examined the results of Geiger and Marsden's experiment in which they had bombarded a very thin sheet of gold with alpha particles. The scientists recorded the pathway of the alpha particles through the gold leaf. To

Rutherford's amazement, he found that while most alpha particles (which are positively charged) passed through the gold atoms undeflected, a small number of alpha particles were deflected a little, and a tiny number of particles were deflected back towards the source. From his observations, Rutherford concluded that the positive charge in the atom must be concentrated in a very small area of the atom. This area is the nucleus of the atom.

The Geiger–Marsden experiment helped Rutherford to devise his 'nuclear' model of the atom

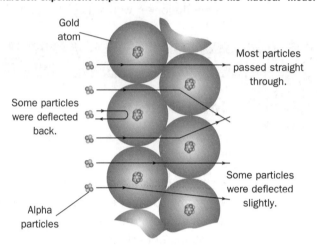

Gold atom

Most particles passed straight through.

Some particles were deflected back.

Some particles were deflected slightly.

Alpha particles

Try designing a timeline to show how ideas about atoms have evolved over time. Include a section for each of the scientists above.

Neils Bohr

In 1913, Neils Bohr deduced that electrons must be found in certain areas in the atom otherwise they would spiral in towards the nucleus.

The modern periodic table

OCR A	C4	✓
OCR B	C4	✓
EDEXCEL	C2	✓

KEY POINT

In the modern periodic table, elements are arranged in order of increasing atomic number.

All the isotopes of an element have the same number of electrons and protons. All the isotopes of an element appear in the same place on the periodic table.

It is called a periodic table because elements with similar properties occur at regular intervals or 'periodically'. The elements are placed in horizontal rows, called **periods**, and elements with similar properties appear in the same vertical column. These vertical columns are called **groups**. The groups may sometimes be numbered using roman numerals, so 'group 3' may be written as 'group III'. The elements in group 1 of the periodic table include lithium, sodium and potassium. All the elements in group 1 of the periodic table share similar properties: they are all metals and they all consist of atoms that have just one electron in their outer shell. When these metals react they form **ions**, which have a 1+ charge. Elements in the same period have the same number of shells of electrons.

PROGRESS CHECK

1. Why do scientists have to re-evaluate existing models?
2. How are the elements arranged in the modern periodic table?
3. What are the horizontal rows in the periodic table called?
4. What are the vertical columns in the periodic table called?
5. John Dalton made a number of predictions about atoms. Today, which of his predictions is not thought to be correct? Explain your answer.

PROGRESS CHECK

different number of neutrons.
are different forms of the same element that have the same number of protons and a
All atoms of the same element are the same. Scientists now know about isotopes. These
that atoms are made of protons, neutrons and electrons.
5. Dalton predicted that atoms cannot be divided into simpler substances. It is now known
4. Groups.
3. Periods.
2. They are in order of increasing atomic number.
1. To check them against new available evidence.

5.3 Chemical reactions and atoms

LEARNING SUMMARY

After studying this section, you should be able to:

- Use symbols to represent the chemical elements.
- Use formulae to represent chemical compounds.
- Interpret a chemical formula in terms of the type and ratio of the atoms that have combined.
- Recall the two different ways atoms can bond together to form compounds.
- Work out the formula of an ionic compound from the electrical charges of the ions.

Symbols

OCR B   C3–C4   ✓
EDEXCEL C2   ✓

In science, elements can be represented by **symbols**. Each element has its own unique symbol that is recognised all over the world. Each symbol consists of one or two letters and is much easier to read and write than the full name. In some cases the symbol for an element is simply the first letter of the element's name. This letter must be a capital letter. The element iodine is represented by the symbol I.

Occasionally an element may take its symbol from its former Latin name. When this happens, the first letter is a capital and the second letter, if there is one, is lower case. The element mercury is represented by the symbol Hg. This comes from the Latin name for mercury, which was *hydrargyrum,* or **liquid silver**.

Several elements have names that start with the same letter. When this happens, the first letter of the element's name is used, together with another letter from the name. The first letter is a capital and the second letter is lower case. The element magnesium is represented by the symbol Mg. The element manganese is represented by the symbol Mn.

> Remember to use your periodic table to check any symbols you are using. Don't forget that if a symbol has two letters, the first letter is a capital and the second is lower case.

Chemical formulae

OCR B	C3–C4	✓
EDEXCEL	C2	✓
WJEC	C2	✓

> **KEY POINT**
>
> A **compound** can be represented using a chemical **formula**. The formula shows the type and ratio of the atoms that are joined together in the compound.

A model of ammonia

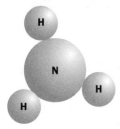

Ammonia has the chemical formula NH_3. This shows that in ammonia, nitrogen and hydrogen atoms are joined together in the ratio of one nitrogen atom to three hydrogen atoms.

You should take care when writing out the symbols for chemical compounds as some of them are very similar to elements. For example:

- The element carbon has the symbol C.
- The element oxygen has the symbol O.
- The element cobalt has the symbol Co.

> Take care when writing formulae with subscript numbers. They will need to be perfect to get the mark awarded in the exam.

The formula CO shows that a carbon atom and an oxygen atom have been chemically combined in a 1 : 1 ratio. This is the formula of the compound carbon monoxide. The symbol Co represents the element cobalt. Notice how the second letter of the symbol is written in lower case. If it wasn't, it would be a completely different substance. The formula CO_2 shows that carbon and oxygen atoms have been chemically combined in a 1 : 2 ratio. This is the formula of the compound carbon dioxide.

Chemical reactions

AQA	C2	✓
OCR B	C3–C4	✓
EDEXCEL	C2	✓
WJEC	C2	✓

An atom

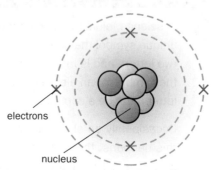

electrons

nucleus

Atoms of different elements can join together by forming new chemical **bonds**.

> **KEY POINT**
>
> Atoms can join together by:
>
> - **covalent bonding** – sharing electrons
> - **ionic bonding** – transferring electrons.

Compounds consist of two or more different types of atom that have been chemically combined. Compounds formed from metals and non-metals consist of ions. These compounds are held together by strong electrostatic forces of attraction. Compounds formed from non-metals consist of molecules. Giant molecules are held together by strong **covalent** bonds.

Word and symbol equations

OCR A	C4	✓
OCR B	C3–C4	✓
EDEXCEL	C2	✓
WJEC	C2	✓

Symbol equations can be used to explain what happens during a chemical reaction. When magnesium burns in air the magnesium metal reacts with the non-metal atoms in oxygen molecules to form the **ionic** compound magnesium oxide. This reaction can be shown in a word equation:

magnesium + oxygen → magnesium oxide

or by the symbol equation:

$2Mg + O_2 \rightarrow 2MgO$

When carbon reacts with oxygen the non-metal carbon atoms react with the non-metal oxygen atoms to form molecules of the covalent compound carbon dioxide. This reaction can be shown in a word equation:

carbon + oxygen → carbon dioxide

or by the symbol equation:

$C + O_2 \rightarrow CO_2$

> **KEY POINT**
>
> Atoms are not created or destroyed during a chemical reaction: the atoms are just rearranged. This means that the total mass of the **reactants** is the same as the total mass of the **products**.

Ionic compounds

AQA	C2	✓
OCR B	C4	✓
EDEXCEL	C2	✓
WJEC	C2	✓

Ionic compounds are formed when a metal reacts with a non-metal. When metal atoms react they lose negatively charged electrons to become positively charged ions (or **cations**). While when non-metal atoms react they gain negatively charged electrons to become negatively charged ions (or **anions**).

There is no overall charge for the ionic compounds so you can use the charge on the ions to work out the formula of the ionic compound.

Metal ions	Non-metal ions
Sodium, Na^+	Bromide, Br^-
Potassium, K^+	Chloride, Cl^-

The compound sodium chloride contains sodium, Na^+, and chloride, Cl^-, ions. For every one sodium ion one chloride ion is required. The overall formula for the compound is NaCl. The compound potassium bromide contains potassium, K^+, and bromide, Br^-, ions. For every one potassium ion one bromide ion is required. The overall formula for the compound is KBr.

> **PROGRESS CHECK**
>
> 1. How can atoms join together?
> 2. Give the name of the element with the symbol Na.
> 3. Give the name of the element with the symbol Cr.
> 4. A water molecule has the formula H_2O. Explain what this formula tells us.

PROGRESS CHECK

5 Sodium nitrate has the formula $NaNO_3$. Explain what this formula tells us.

6 Give the formula for the following compounds:
   a) Potassium chloride.
   b) Sodium bromide.

1. Atoms can be joined by sharing electrons or by transferring electrons.
2. Sodium.
3. Chromium.
4. It consists of 2 hydrogen atoms and 1 oxygen atom.
5. It consists of sodium atoms, nitrogen atoms and oxygen atoms in the ratio 1 : 1 : 3.
6. a) KCl.
   b) NaBr.

5.4 The periodic table

LEARNING SUMMARY

After studying this section, you should be able to:

- Recall that Dobereiner's triads and Newlands' octaves were early attempts to show patterns in the properties of elements.
- Understand the reasoning behind Mendeleev's arrangement of the elements.
- Recognise the strengths and weaknesses of Mendeleev's Periodic Table.
- Understand the significance of groups and periods in relation to electron arrangements.
- Recall some of the properties of the transition elements.

Early ideas

OCR A	C4	✓
OCR B	C4	✓
EDEXCEL	C2	✓

As new **elements** were discovered, scientists struggled to find links between them. In 1829, the German chemist Johann Wolfgang Dobereiner noticed that many elements could be put into groups of three, which he called **triads**. If these elements were placed in order of **atomic weight**, the atomic weight of the middle element was about the average of the lighter and the heavier elements. He noticed a similar pattern when he compared the densities of the members of a triad. Unfortunately, this pattern only appeared to work for some groups of elements.

Key developments

OCR A	C4	✓
OCR B	C4	✓
EDEXCEL	C2	✓

In 1863, the English chemist John Newlands, noticed that if the known elements were placed in order of their atomic weight, and then put into rows of seven, there were strong similarities between elements in the same vertical column i.e. each element was similar to the one eight places on. This pattern became known as **Newlands' law of octaves**. It was useful for some of the elements but unfortunately Newlands' pattern broke down when he tried to include the **transition elements**.

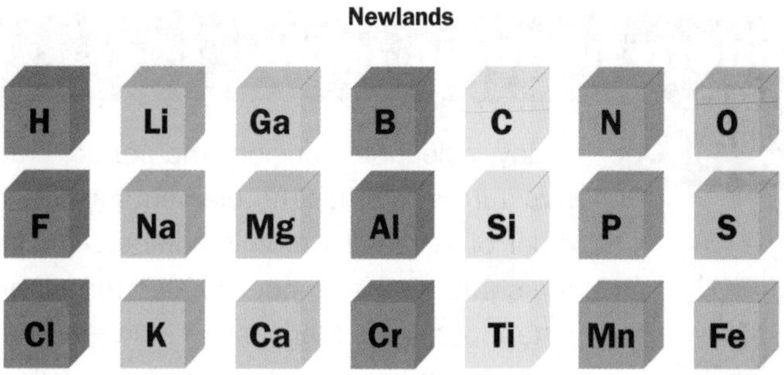

Newlands

H	Li	Ga	B	C	N	O
F	Na	Mg	Al	Si	P	S
Cl	K	Ca	Cr	Ti	Mn	Fe

The **noble gases** are not shown in the diagram. They were only discovered in the 1890s when chemists noticed that the density of nitrogen made in reactions was slightly different from the density of nitrogen obtained directly from the air. The chemists thought the air might contain small amounts of other gases and so they devised experiments that eventually confirmed the presence of the very **unreactive** noble gases. They found that the air includes nitrogen, oxygen, neon and argon.

Mendeleev's idea

OCR A	C4	✓
OCR B	C4	✓
EDEXCEL	C2	✓

In 1869, the Russian chemist Dimitri **Mendeleev** produced his periodic table of elements. In his table, elements with similar properties occurred periodically and were placed in vertical columns called **groups**. Like Newlands, Mendeleev arranged the elements in order of increasing atomic weight, but unlike Newlands he did not stick strictly to this order.

> **KEY POINT**
>
> He left gaps for elements that had yet to be discovered, such as germanium and gallium, and made detailed predictions about the physical and chemical **properties** these elements would have.

Mendeleev was not aware of protons, neutrons or electrons as they were not discovered until much later. Make sure you do not say he knew about them when you are answering exam questions.

Eventually, when these elements were discovered and their properties analysed, scientists were impressed by the accuracy of Mendeleev's predictions. Mendeleev's table went from being an interesting curiosity to a useful tool for understanding how a particular element would behave. Mendeleev would sometimes swap the order of the elements if their properties suggested it would be right to do so.

Atomic number

AQA	C2	✓
OCR A	C4	✓
OCR B	C4	✓
EDEXCEL	C2	✓
WJEC	C2	✓

By leaving gaps and swapping the order of the elements, Mendeleev had actually arranged the elements in order of **increasing atomic number** (or number of protons in the nucleus of an atom), even though protons themselves were not discovered until much later. In fact, electrons, protons and neutrons were all discovered in the early 20th century.

The modern periodic table

OCR B   C4   ✓
EDEXCEL   C2   ✓

Today, scientists consider the periodic table an important summary of the structure of atoms. The elements in the modern periodic table are arranged in order of increasing atomic number. The group that the element belongs to is the same as the number of electrons that each atom of that element has in its outermost shell. Magnesium is in group 2 of the periodic table, so an atom of magnesium has two electrons in its outermost shell. Oxygen is in group 6 of the periodic table, so an atom of oxygen has six electrons in its outermost shell. The noble gases have a full outermost shell of electrons and no electrons at all in the next shell, so they all belong to group 0. The vertical rows are called periods. The period the element belongs to indicates the number of shells that are occupied by electrons for an atom of that element. A detailed periodic table can be used to find the names, symbols, relative atomic masses and atomic number of any element.

The modern periodic table is arranged in order of increasing atomic number. You must make this clear in your answers. Many students refer to increasing mass number, which is not correct.

Transition metals

OCR B   C4   ✓
EDEXCEL   C2   ✓

The transition metals are found in the central block of the periodic table. The transition metals are much less reactive than group 1 metals. Transition metals have high melting points so, with the exception of mercury, are solid at room temperature. They are hard and strong and make useful structural materials. They do not react with water or oxygen as vigorously as group 1 metals, although many will show signs of corrosion over long periods of time.

Transition metal ions

OCR B   C4   ✓

When transition metals form compounds the transition metal ions have **variable charges**. For example, in copper(II) oxide, CuO, the copper ions have a 2+ charge, while in copper(I) oxide, Cu_2O, the copper ions have a 1+ charge. The roman numerals given in the name of the transition metal compound shows the charge on the transition metal ion. Transition metal compounds are coloured; group 1 and 2 metal compounds are white. Transition metals and transition metal compounds are useful catalysts (chemicals that speed up chemical reactions). Iron is used in the Haber process (which produces ammonia) while nickel is used in the hydrogenation of ethene.

PROGRESS CHECK

1. What is the name given to Mendeleev's way of arranging the elements?
2. Why did Mendeleev not include the element germanium in his arrangement of the elements?
3. What group does magnesium belong to?
4. What group does oxygen belong to?
5. What is the charge on the copper ion in the compound copper(II) oxide?

5.5 Balancing equations

LEARNING SUMMARY

After studying this section, you should be able to:

- Recall that mass is always conserved in chemical reactions.
- Understand the advantage of using a symbol equation over a word equation.
- Decide if an equation is balanced, by counting atoms on both sides.
- Balance an equation that is not balanced, by adding numbers in front of symbols.
- Understand the use of state symbols in a chemical equation.

Conservation of mass

OCR A	C6	✓
OCR B	C3–C4	✓
EDEXCEL	C2	✓

Symbol equations show the type and ratio of the atoms involved in a reaction. The **reactants** are placed on the left-hand side of the equation. The **products** are placed on the right-hand side of the equation. Overall, mass is **conserved** because atoms are never made or destroyed during chemical reactions. This means that there must always be the same number of each type of atom on both sides of the equation.

Reactants	$\longrightarrow$	Products
Magnesium + Oxygen	$\longrightarrow$	Magnesium Oxide
2Mg(s) + O$_2$(g)	$\longrightarrow$	**2MgO(s)**

Balancing the equation

OCR A	C4–C6	✓
OCR B	C3–C4	✓
EDEXCEL	C2	✓

Hydrogen burns in air to produce water vapour. This can be shown using a word equation.

Hydrogen + Oxygen → Water

The word equation is useful but it doesn't give the ratio of hydrogen and oxygen molecules involved. Balanced symbol equations show this extra information. First, replace the words with symbols. Hydrogen and oxygen both exist as molecules.

$$H_2 + O_2 \rightarrow H_2O$$

The formulae are all correct, but the equation does not balance because there are different numbers of atoms on each side of the equation. The formulae cannot be changed, but numbers can be added in front of the formulae to balance the equation.

The equation shows that there are two oxygen atoms on the left-hand side of the equation but only one oxygen atom on the right-hand side.

A number 2 is therefore placed in front of the H_2O:

$$H_2 + O_2 \rightarrow 2H_2O$$

Now the oxygen atoms are balanced: there is the same number of oxygen atoms on both sides of the equation. However, the hydrogen atoms are no longer balanced. There are two hydrogen atoms on the left-hand side and four hydrogen atoms on the right-hand side. So a 2 is placed in front of the H_2:

$$2H_2 + O_2 \rightarrow 2H_2O$$

> To get a top mark, you need to be able to balance equations. This skill just needs a little practice. Deal with each type of atom in turn until everything balances.
>
> Remember to write any subscripts below the line:
>
> H_2O is correct while H^2O and H2O are wrong.

The equation is now balanced.

State symbols

AQA   C2   ✓
OCR A   C4–C6   ✓
EDEXCEL C2   ✓

State symbols can be added to an equation to show extra information. They show what physical state the reactants and products are in. The symbols are:

- (s) for solid
- (l) for liquid
- (g) for gases
- (aq) for aqueous, or dissolved in water.

> Aqueous comes from the Latin *aqua* meaning water. Aqueous means dissolved in water.

Magnesium metal can be burned in air to produce magnesium oxide. Magnesium and magnesium oxide are both solids. The part of the air that reacts when things are burned is oxygen, which is a gas.

magnesium + oxygen → magnesium oxide

$$2Mg(s) + O_2(g) \rightarrow 2MgO(s)$$

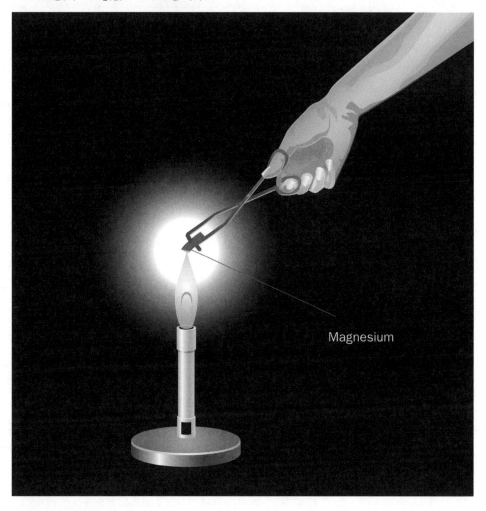

Magnesium

KEY POINT

When balancing equations, always check that the formulae you have written down are correct.

Some equations involve formulae that contain brackets, for example, calcium hydroxide: $Ca(OH)_2$. This means that calcium hydroxide contains calcium, oxygen and hydrogen atoms in the ratio 1 : 2 : 2. These equations can be balanced normally. Calcium reacts with water to form calcium hydroxide, which is slightly soluble, and hydrogen gas.

calcium + water → calcium hydroxide + hydrogen

$$Ca(s) + 2H_2O(l) \rightarrow Ca(OH)_2(aq) + H_2(g)$$

Precipitation reactions

AQA	C2	✓
OCR A	C5	✓
OCR B	C4	✓
EDEXCEL	C2	✓

Some insoluble salts can be made from the reaction between two solutions. Barium sulfate is an insoluble salt. It can be made by the reaction between solutions of barium chloride and sodium sulfate.

barium chloride + sodium sulfate → barium sulfate + sodium chloride

$$BaCl_2(aq) + Na_2SO_4(aq) \rightarrow BaSO_4(s) + 2NaCl(aq)$$

Understanding precipitation reactions

AQA	C2	✓
OCR A	C5	✓
OCR B	C4	✓
EDEXCEL	C2	✓

The insoluble barium sulfate can be filtered off, washed and dried. Overall, the two original salts, barium chloride and sodium sulfate, have swapped partners. Barium chloride solution can be used to test whether a solution contains sulfate ions. If sulfate ions are present, a white precipitate of barium sulfate will be seen. The chloride ions and sodium ions are **spectator ions**. They are present but they are not involved in the reaction. The ionic equation for the reaction is:

$$Ba^{2+}(aq) + SO_4{}^{2-}(aq) \rightarrow BaSO_4(s)$$

Precipitation reactions are very fast. When the reactant solutions are mixed, the reacting ions collide together very quickly and react together to form the insoluble solid.

Barium sulfate is used in medicine as a **barium meal**. The patient is given the insoluble salt and then X-rayed. The barium sulfate is opaque to X-rays so doctors can detect digestive problems without having to carry out an operation. Although barium salts are toxic, barium sulfate is so insoluble that very little dissolves and passes into the bloodstream of the patient.

PROGRESS CHECK

1. Why must there be the same number of each type of atom on both sides of an equation?
2. Balance the equation $Na + Cl_2 \rightarrow NaCl$.
3. Balance the equation $H_2 + Cl_2 \rightarrow HCl$.
4. Balance the equation $C + CO_2 \rightarrow CO$.
5. What does the state symbol (l) indicate?
6. Explain why precipitation reactions happen very quickly.

6. The reacting ions collide together and react very quickly
5. It is a liquid.
4. $C + CO_2 \rightarrow 2CO$.
3. $H_2 + Cl_2 \rightarrow 2HCl$.
2. $2Na + Cl_2 \rightarrow 2NaCl$.
1. Atoms cannot be created or destroyed during chemical reactions.

5.6 Ionic and covalent bonding

LEARNING SUMMARY

After studying this section, you should be able to:

- Describe the differences between ionic and covalent bonding.
- Predict the type of ion formed, by looking at electron arrangements.
- Draw diagrams to show the ionic bonding in simple ionic compounds.
- Explain how non-metal atoms bond by sharing pairs of electrons.
- Draw diagrams to show electron sharing in simple covalent molecules.

Types of bonding

AQA	C2	✓
OCR A	C5	✓
OCR B	C3–C4	✓
EDEXCEL	C2	✓
WJEC	C2	✓

Compounds are made when **atoms** of two or more **elements** are chemically combined. **Ionic bonding** involves the transfer of **electrons** in the outermost shell of atoms. This forms **ions** with opposite charges, which then attract each other. Ions are atoms or groups of atoms with a charge. **Covalent bonding** involves the sharing of electrons. The attraction of the nuclei for shared pairs of electrons hold the atoms together.

Ionic bonding

AQA	C2	✓
OCR A	C5	✓
OCR B	C3–C4	✓
EDEXCEL	C2	✓
WJEC	C2	✓

> **KEY POINT**
>
> Atoms react to get a full outer shell of electrons (like the noble gas elements). Ionic bonding involves the transfer of electrons from one atom to another.

Metal atoms in groups 1 and 2, such as sodium or calcium, lose electrons to get a full outer shell of electrons. Overall, they become positively charged. (Electrons have a negative charge). Non-metal atoms in groups 6 and 7, such as oxygen or chlorine, gain electrons to get a full outer shell. They become negatively charged. An ion is an atom, or a group of atoms, with a charge. An atom, or group of atoms, becomes an ion by gaining or losing electrons. The positive and negative ions formed have the same electronic structure as a noble gas atom.

Ionic compounds

AQA	C2	✓
OCR A	C4, C5	✓
OCR B	C3–C4	✓
EDEXCEL	C2	✓
WJEC	C2	✓

Compound	Diagram	Comments
sodium + chlorine → sodium chloride	In the dot and cross diagrams, the electrons drawn as dots, and the electrons drawn as crosses, are identical. They are drawn like this so it is easier to see what happens when the electrons move.	The sodium atom transfers one electron from its outer shell to the chlorine atom. Both the sodium and chlorine atom have a full outer shell. The sodium atom has lost a negatively charged electron so it now has a 1+ charge and is called a sodium ion. The chlorine atom has gained an electron so has a 1- charge. It is now a chloride ion. The attraction between these two oppositely charged ions is called an ionic bond and it holds the compound together.

Compound	Diagram	Comments
magnesium + oxygen → magnesium oxide	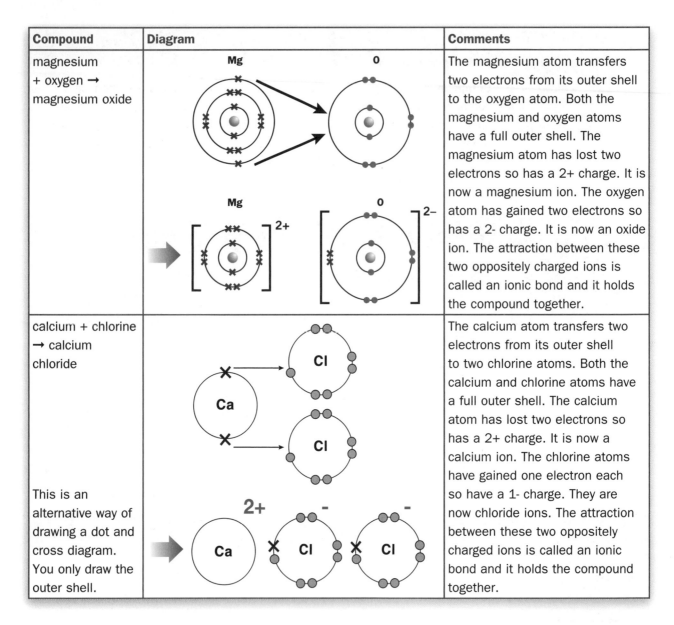	The magnesium atom transfers two electrons from its outer shell to the oxygen atom. Both the magnesium and oxygen atoms have a full outer shell. The magnesium atom has lost two electrons so has a 2+ charge. It is now a magnesium ion. The oxygen atom has gained two electrons so has a 2- charge. It is now an oxide ion. The attraction between these two oppositely charged ions is called an ionic bond and it holds the compound together.
calcium + chlorine → calcium chloride

This is an alternative way of drawing a dot and cross diagram. You only draw the outer shell. | | The calcium atom transfers two electrons from its outer shell to two chlorine atoms. Both the calcium and chlorine atoms have a full outer shell. The calcium atom has lost two electrons so has a 2+ charge. It is now a calcium ion. The chlorine atoms have gained one electron each so have a 1- charge. They are now chloride ions. The attraction between these two oppositely charged ions is called an ionic bond and it holds the compound together. |

Sodium oxide has the formula Na_2O. Both sodium atoms transfer one electron to the same oxygen atom. The sodium ions each have a 1+ charge while the oxide ion has a 2- charge.

Covalent bonding

AQA	C2	✓
OCR A	C5	✓
OCR B	C3–C4	✓
EDEXCEL	C2	✓
WJEC	C2	✓

KEY POINT

Covalent bonding occurs between atoms of non-metal elements. The atoms share pairs of electrons so that all the atoms gain a full outer shell of electrons.

There is an **electrostatic attraction** between the nuclei of the atoms and the pair of bonding electrons.

Covalent molecules

AQA   C2   ✓
OCR A   C4   ✓
OCR B   C3–C4   ✓
EDEXCEL   C2   ✓
WJEC   C2   ✓

Compound	Diagram of molecule	Comments
Hydrogen		Both the hydrogen atoms have just one electron. Both atoms can get a full outer shell by sharing these electrons to form a single covalent bond.
Hydrogen chloride		The hydrogen atom and the chlorine atom both need one more electron. They share a pair of electrons to form a single covalent bond, so they now both have a full outer shell.
Methane		The carbon atom has four electrons in its outer shell so it needs four more electrons to have a full shell. The carbon shares one pair of electrons with four different hydrogen atoms to form four single covalent bonds. Now all the atoms have a full outer shell.
Ammonia		The nitrogen atom has five outer electrons so it needs three more electrons for a full shell. It gains these electrons by sharing a pair of electrons with three hydrogen atoms to form three single covalent bonds.
Oxygen		Both oxygen atoms have six outer electrons so they need a share of two more electrons. They gain these by sharing two pairs of electrons to form a double covalent bond.

PROGRESS CHECK

1. What are ions?
2. What holds the atoms together in covalent molecules?
3. What happens to electrons during ionic bonding?
4. What type of atom is oxygen?
5. Name and describe the type of bonding that you would expect to find in these substances:
   a) Oxygen O_2.
   b) Sodium chloride, NaCl.

PROGRESS CHECK

1. Atoms or groups of atoms with a charge.
2. Shared pairs of electrons.
3. Electrons are transferred.
4. Non-metal.
5. a) Covalent bonding, with a double covalent bond between the two oxygen atoms.
   b) Ionic bonding between the positively charged sodium ions and the negatively charged chloride ions.

5.7 Ionic and covalent structures

LEARNING SUMMARY

After studying this section, you should be able to:

- Describe ionic bonding and compounds.
- Describe simple covalent structures and their properties.
- Describe giant covalent structures and their properties.
- Describe the structure and properties of diamond.
- Describe the structure and properties of graphite.

Ionic bonding

AQA	C2	✓
OCR A	C4	✓
OCR B	C3–C4	✓
EDEXCEL	C2	✓
WJEC	C2	✓

KEY POINT

Ionic bonding occurs between metal and non-metal atoms. It involves the transfer of **electrons** and the formation of **ions**.

Sodium chloride and magnesium oxide are examples of ionic compounds. The ions are arranged in a regular 'lattice' with each positive ion surrounded by negative ions and vice versa.

Ionic compounds

AQA	C2	✓
OCR A	C4–C5	✓
OCR B	C3–C4	✓
EDEXCEL	C2	✓
WJEC	C2	✓

- **Ionic compounds** are held together by the strong forces of attraction between oppositely charged ions (electrostatic attraction).
- Ionic compounds have a regular structure.
- The **strong** forces of attraction between oppositely charged ions work in all directions and this means that ionic compounds have high melting and boiling points.
- When dissolved in water, ionic compounds form solutions in which the ions can move. This means that these solutions can **conduct** electricity.
- Similarly, if ionic compounds are heated up so that they melt, the ions can move. Molten ionic compounds can also conduct electricity.

Simple covalent structures

AQA	C2	✓
OCR A	C5	✓
OCR B	C4	✓
EDEXCEL	C2	✓
WJEC	C2	✓

Covalent bonding occurs between non-metal atoms. It involves the sharing of electrons. Examples of simple covalent structures include:

- chlorine molecules
- oxygen molecules
- hydrogen iodide molecules
- methane molecules
- water molecules
- carbon dioxide molecules.

These **molecules** are all formed from small numbers of atoms.

Important properties of simple molecular compounds

AQA	C2	✓
OCR A	C5	✓
OCR B	C4	✓
EDEXCEL	C2	✓
WJEC	C2	✓

> **KEY POINT**
>
> There are very strong covalent bonds between the atoms in each molecule, but very weak forces of attraction between these molecules.

The low boiling points of simple molecules is due to the weak forces of attraction *between* molecules.

This means that simple molecular compounds have low melting and boiling points. Most are gases or liquids at room temperature. Simple molecular compounds do not conduct electricity because, unlike ions, the molecules do not have an overall electrical charge. They tend to be **insoluble** in water (although they may dissolve in water and other solvents).

To help you learn the facts you need for the exam, make a table to compare the features of ionic and covalent structures.

Giant covalent structures

AQA	C2	✓
OCR A	C5	✓
OCR B	C3	✓
EDEXCEL	C2	✓
WJEC	C2	✓

Examples of giant covalent (macromolecular) structures include:

- diamond
- graphite
- silicon dioxide.

These structures are formed from a large number of atoms. All the atoms in these structures are held together by **strong covalent bonds**. This means that these substances have **high melting and boiling points**. They are solids at room temperature. Like simple covalent molecules, giant covalent substances do not conduct electricity (except graphite) as they do not contain ions. They are also **insoluble** in water.

Diamond

AQA	C2	✓
OCR A	C5	✓
OCR B	C3	✓
EDEXCEL	C2	✓
WJEC	C2	✓

Diamond is a form of the element carbon. Like other gemstones, it is prized for its rarity and its pleasing appearance: it is lustrous, colourless and transparent. Diamond is also very hard. High quality diamonds are used to make jewellery. Other diamonds are used in industry in a variety of applications. The hardness and high melting point of diamond makes it very suitable for cutting tools. The special properties of diamond are the result of its **structure**. Diamond is an example of a giant covalent substance. Each carbon atom is bonded to four other carbon atoms by strong covalent bonds. It takes a lot of energy to break these strong bonds. Diamond is a very poor electrical conductor because it does not have any free electrons.

Diamond structure

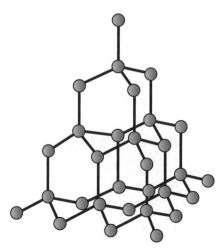

Graphite

AQA	C2	✓
OCR A	C5	✓
OCR B	C3	✓
EDEXCEL	C2	✓
WJEC	C2	✓

Graphite is another **allotrope** of the element carbon. Allotropes are different forms of the same element in the same physical state. Diamond, graphite and fullerene are all allotropes of carbon. Graphite is black, lustrous and opaque. It is used to make pencil 'leads' because the layers slip apart easily, so when a pencil is rubbed on paper a black mark is left. It is also used in lubricants because it is slippery and allows surfaces to pass over each other more easily.

In graphite, each carbon atom forms strong covalent bonds with three other carbon atoms in the same layer. However, the bonding between layers is much weaker. This means that the layers can pass over each other quite easily, which is why graphite is soft and feels greasy. If a potential difference is applied across graphite the electrons in the weak bonds between layers move and so conduct electricity. Carbon in the form of graphite is the only non-metal element that conducts electricity. It also has a very high melting point because a lot of energy is required to break these strong covalent bonds. These properties make it a suitable material from which to make electrodes.

> **PROGRESS CHECK**
>
> 1. What type of structure is magnesium oxide?
> 2. What type of structure is graphite?
> 3. What type of structure is methane?
> 4. What type of structure is diamond?
> 5. Sodium chloride is an ionic compound. It does not conduct electricity when solid but does when it is dissolved in water. Explain these observations in terms of the particles involved.

5.8 Group 7

LEARNING SUMMARY	**After studying this section, you should be able to:**
	• Recall that elements in group 7 have seven outer-shell electrons.
	• Describe trends in physical properties of group 7 elements.
	• Recall the uses of some halogen elements.
	• Describe and explain the trend in reactivity of the halogens.
	• Use differences in reactivity to explain halogen displacement reactions.

The halogens

AQA	C2	✓
OCR A	C4	✓
OCR B	C4	✓
EDEXCEL	C2	✓
WJEC	C2	✓

The elements in group 7 are known as the **halogens**. The atoms of group 7 elements all have seven electrons in their outermost shell. When halogen atoms react they gain an electron to form **halide ions**.

Characteristics of the halogens

OCR A	C4	✓
OCR B	C4	✓
EDEXCEL	C2	✓
WJEC	C2	✓

Down the group, the melting points and boiling points of the halogens increase, so fluorine and chlorine are gases at room temperature while bromine is a liquid and iodine is a solid. Halogens react with hydrogen to form hydrogen halides, for example, chlorine reacts with hydrogen to form hydrogen chloride. Hydrogen halides dissolve in water to form acidic solutions.

Halogens

5	6	7	0
			He Helium
	O Oxygen	F Fluorine	Ne Neon
	S Sulfur	Cl Chlorine	Ar Argon
	Se Selenium	Br Bromine	Kr Krypton
	Te Tellurium	I Iodine	Xe Xenon
	Po Polonium	At Astatine	Rn Radon

The halogen family includes fluorine, chlorine, bromine and iodine. Halogens have coloured vapours. The colour gets darker further down the group.

Halogen	Comments
Fluorine	Fluorine is a very poisonous gas that should only be used in a **fume cupboard**. Fluorine is a **diatomic** (two atoms joined together) molecule with the formula F_2. It has a pale yellow colour. Sodium fluoride is added to toothpastes and to some water supplies to help prevent tooth decay. Scientists carried out large studies to prove that adding fluoride compounds was effective at protecting teeth, but some people are concerned over the lack of choice those living in affected areas now have.
Chlorine	Chlorine is a poisonous gas that should only be used in a fume cupboard. Chlorine is a diatomic molecule with the formula Cl_2. It has a pale green colour. Chlorine kills bacteria and is used in water purification. It is also used to make plastics and pesticides and in **bleaching**. In the past, chlorine and iodine were extracted from compounds found in seawater. However, it is no longer economically worthwhile to extract iodine in this way.
Bromine	Bromine is a poisonous, dense liquid. It has a brown colour. Bromine is a diatomic molecule, Br_2.
Iodine	Iodine exists as a dark grey crystalline solid. Solid iodine is brittle and crumbly. Solid iodine is a poor electrical and thermal conductor. Iodine forms a purple vapour when warmed. Iodine solution can be used as an antiseptic to sterilise wounds as it kills bacteria. Iodine solution can be used to test for the presence of starch. When iodine solution is placed on a material that contains starch it turns blue/black. Iodine is a diatomic molecule, I_2.
Astatine	Astatine is also in group 7 of the periodic table; it is found just below iodine. We can use the physical properties of the other halogens to predict the properties of astatine. It will be a dark coloured solid at room temperature.

Be careful not to write chloride if you mean chlorine.

To help you learn the facts about halogens, try making a poster with a different section for each member of the group.

Why halogens react in a similar way

AQA	C2	✓
OCR A	C4	✓
OCR B	C4	✓
EDEXCEL	C2	✓
WJEC	C2	✓

KEY POINT

Halogens have seven electrons in their outer shell. Group 7 elements have similar properties because they all have similar electron structures. Halogens react with metal atoms to form ionic compounds.

For example, chlorine reacts with potassium to form potassium chloride.

chlorine + potassium → potassium chloride

$$2K + Cl_2 \rightarrow 2KCl$$

Reduction

OCR A	C4	✓
OCR B	C4	✓
EDEXCEL	C2	✓
WJEC	C2	✓

When they react, a halogen atom gains an electron to form an ion with a 1– charge.

$$Cl + e^- \rightarrow Cl^-$$

A reduction reaction has taken place. The halogen atom has gained an electron so it is **reduced**.

Important trends

OCR A	C4	✓
OCR B	C4	✓
EDEXCEL	C2	✓
WJEC	C2	✓

Melting and boiling points increase down the group. Group 7 atoms form molecules in which two atoms are joined together. These are called diatomic molecules.

Down the group, the atoms get larger and have more electrons. This means that the strength of the attraction between molecules increases. As the forces of attraction between molecules get stronger down the group, it takes more energy to overcome these forces so the halogens will melt and boil at higher temperatures.

Why fluorine reacts more vigorously than bromine

OCR A	C4	✓
OCR B	C4	✓
EDEXCEL	C2	✓
WJEC	C2	✓

Reactivity decreases down the group: when an atom reacts to form an **ion**, the new electron is being placed into a shell further away from the nucleus. So, down the group, it is harder for atoms to gain an electron. There are also more shells of electrons shielding the new electron from the nucleus. This also makes it harder for atoms to gain a new electron further down the group. This pattern is clearly shown by the reaction between the halogens and iron wool to form iron halides.

> Chlorine is more reactive than bromine and iodine.

Halogen used	Observations
Chlorine	Iron glows very brightly. A brown smoke is given off and a brown solid is formed.
Bromine	The iron glows. Brown smoke is given off and a brown solid is formed.
Iodine	The iron glows a little. Brown smoke is given off and a brown solid is formed.

Reactivity of halogens

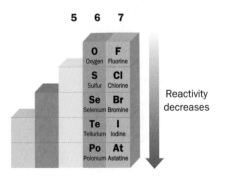

Displacement reactions involving halogens

OCR A	C4	✓
OCR B	C4	✓
EDEXCEL	C2	✓
WJEC	C2	✓

KEY POINT

Reactivity decreases down group 7. The most reactive halogen is fluorine, followed by chlorine, then bromine, then iodine.

A more reactive halogen will **displace** (that is, take the place of) a less reactive halogen from an aqueous solution of its salt. So, chlorine could displace bromine or iodine. However, while bromine could displace iodine it could not displace chlorine.

Symbol equations

OCR A	C4	✓
OCR B	C3–C4	✓
EDEXCEL	C2	✓
WJEC	C2	✓

Chlorine will displace iodine from a solution of potassium iodide.

chlorine + potassium iodide → iodine + potassium chloride

$$Cl_2 + 2KI \rightarrow I_2 + 2KCl$$

The reaction between chlorine and potassium iodide

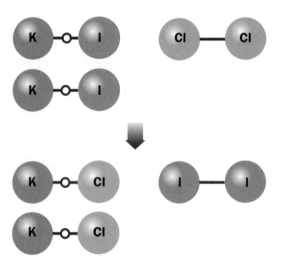

PROGRESS CHECK

1. What is the name given to group 7 of the periodic table?
2. How is a halide ion formed?
3. What type of compound is formed when a metal reacts with a halogen?
4. What is the name of the compound made when chlorine reacts with potassium?
5. Chlorine gas is passed through an aqueous solution of potassium iodide. Write a word and symbol equation to sum up this reaction. Remember to include state symbols in your answer.

1. Halogens.
2. When a halogen atom gains an electron
3. Ionic compound/metal halide.
4. Potassium chloride.
5. chlorine + potassium iodide → iodine + potassium chloride
$Cl_2(g) + 2KI(aq) \rightarrow I_2(aq) + 2KCl(aq)$

5.9 Nanoparticles

LEARNING SUMMARY

After studying this section, you should be able to:

- Understand the properties of nanomaterials.
- Relate the properties of nanomaterials to their uses.

Nanoparticles

AQA   C2   ✓

KEY POINT

Nanoscience is the study of extremely small pieces of material called nanoparticles.

Scientists are currently researching the properties of new nanoparticles. These are substances that contain just a few hundred atoms and vary in size from 1 nm (nanometre) to 100 nm so they are the same size as some molecules (human hair has a width of about 100 000 nm). Nanoparticles occur in nature and are found in sea spray. They can also be made either accidentally, for example, when fuels are burned, or very deliberately.

In nanomaterials, the atoms themselves are not smaller. When you answer exam questions, make sure you do not infer that the atoms have changed size.

Nanomaterials have unique properties because of the very precise way in which the atoms are arranged. Scientists have found that many materials behave differently on such a small scale.

Scientists are using nanoparticles to develop very lightweight materials. These materials are incredibly hard and strong because of the precise way that the atoms are arranged. One day these materials could be used to build planes.

Nanoparticles have a very high surface area to volume ratio. Scientists hope that this will allow them to use nanoparticles in exciting ways such as:

- In new computers
- in sunscreens and deodorants
- in drug delivery systems
- better catalysts. Catalysts are substances that speed up the rate of a chemical reaction but are not themselves used up. Reactions take place at the surface of the catalyst. The larger the surface area of the catalyst the more reactions can take place at once and the better the catalyst performs.

Scientists are also keen to explore the use of nanoparticles as sensors to detect biological or chemical agents at very low levels. They may also be used to make battery electrodes for electric vehicles or solar cells.

Nanoscale silver particles have antibacterial, antiviral and antifungal properties. These tiny pieces of silver are incorporated into materials to make clothes and medical dressings stay fresh for longer.

Try producing a set of revision cards to learn the important ideas in this topic.

There has recently been a great deal of media interest in the development and applications of new nanoparticles. Some scientists are concerned that certain nanoparticles could be dangerous to people because their exceptionally small size may mean they are able to pass into the body in previously unimaginable ways, and could go on to cause health problems.

Buckminster fullerene, C₆₀

| AQA | C2 | ✓ |
| OCR B | C3 | ✓ |

The element carbon exists in three forms or allotropes:

- graphite
- diamond
- fullerenes.

Fullerenes are structures made when carbon atoms join together to form tubes, balls or cages, which are held together by strong covalent bonds. The most symmetrical and, therefore, most stable example is buckminster fullerene. This consists of 60 carbon atoms joined together in a series of hexagons and pentagons, much like a leather football.

Structure of buckminster fullerene

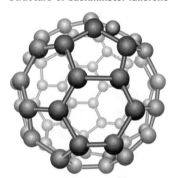

Learn the formula for buckminster fullerene: C_{60}

PROGRESS CHECK

1. How big are nanoparticles?
2. What is the formula of buckminster fullerene?
3. Where are nanoparticles found in nature?

3. In sea spray.
2. C_{60}.
1. 1 nm–100 nm.

5.10 Synthesis

LEARNING SUMMARY

After studying this section, you should be able to:

- Understand that making new chemicals involves many stages.
- Describe the differences between batch and continuous manufacturing processes.
- Recall that plants are often good sources of chemicals.
- Understand the economics and licensing involved in developing a new medicine.
- List the factors affecting the long-term sustainability of a chemical process.

Making new chemicals

| OCR A | C6 | ✓ |
| OCR B | C3 | ✓ |

The manufacture of useful chemicals involves many stages. **Raw materials** need to be selected and prepared, and then the new chemicals have to be made in a process known as **synthesis**. Next, the useful products have to be separated from **by-products** and waste, each of which must also be dealt with. Finally, the **purity** of the product must be checked.

Batch or continuous production

OCR B   C3   ✓

Some chemicals are made in **batch processes**.

> **KEY POINT**
>
> Batch processes are used to make relatively small amounts of special chemicals such as medicines. The chemicals are made when they are needed rather than all the time.
>
> **Continuous processes** are used to make chemicals that are needed in large amounts, such as sulfuric acid or ammonia.

The chemicals are made all the time. Raw materials are continuously added and new products are removed.

Some chemicals, such as ammonia, sulfuric acid, sodium hydroxide and phosphoric acid, are made in **bulk** (on a large scale). Other chemicals, such as medicines, food additives and fragrances, are described as being made on a **fine** scale (a small scale).

Governments regulate how chemicals are made, stored and transported to protect people and the environment from accidental damage.

Medicines from plants

OCR B   C3   ✓

Scientists can **extract** chemicals from plants or produce them synthetically. Chemicals can be extracted from plants by:

Make a flow diagram to show the stages involved in extracting chemicals from plants.

- Crushing up the plant material.
- Adding a suitable solvent and then heating the mixture so that the useful chemicals dissolve in the solvent.
- Using separation techniques, such as chromatography, to separate out mixtures of compounds. Chromatography separates mixtures according to differences in solubility of the components.

Plant materials can be used to make very useful medicines. Digitalin medicines are extracted from foxglove plants and are used to treat heart conditions.

Digitalin can be extracted from foxglove plants

Morphine is made from opium poppies and is used for pain relief.

Opium poppy pod and seeds, from which morphine can be made

Making and developing new medicines

OCR B   C3   ✓

New medicines are often very expensive to buy because of the high costs of **developing** and making the drugs. The factors that affect the price of a medicine include:

- Labour and energy costs. The production of new medicines is often very labour intensive as little automation is possible, at least initially.
- The cost of the raw materials required, which may be very rare or expensive.
- The time required for researching and developing new drugs. These processes can take many years.
- Testing of the new medicine. It must pass all the testing stages and human trials required by law for it to gain a licence to be sold. This takes a lot of time and money.
- Marketing of the medicine. Companies have to let the medical profession know the benefits of the new medicine and why they should consider giving it to their patients.

Economic considerations

OCR B   C3   ✓

Scientists developing new drugs need to be aware of economic considerations. The more research and development involved the more expensive the new medicine will be. Scientists need to work out if there is sufficient demand for the new medicine for it to pay back the considerable investment needed to produce it. New drugs only have a patent for a certain length of time. Companies that manufacture the medicine pay money to the people who hold the patent and who did the initial research and development for the drug. If the time limit for the patent is set too low, the patent will have run out before the initial costs have been paid back.

Green chemistry

OCR B   C3   ✓

Addition reactions (when two chemicals are added together), such as the reaction between ethene and steam to produce ethanol, will have an atom economy of 100%

The long-term sustainability of a chemical process depends on:

- whether or not the raw materials are renewable
- the atom economy of the reactions involved
- the amount and nature of waste produced
- the amount and nature of by-products produced
- energy requirements
- impact on the environment
- health and safety risks
- the economic and social benefits of the products made by the reaction.

PROGRESS CHECK

1. Why are the labour costs for new medicines often very high?
2. Why do new drugs have to be marketed?
3. Name a separation technique that separates out mixtures because the components have different solubilities.
4. Name two types of medicine that are made using plant extracts.
5. Describe the steps involved in extracting chemicals from plants.
6. Describe what happens during a continuous process.

1. Little automation is possible, at least initially.
2. To let the medical profession know the benefits of the new medicine and why they should consider giving it to their patients.
3. Chromatography.
4. Digitalin medicines and morphine.
5. Crush up the plant material. Add a suitable solvent and then heat the mixture so that the useful chemicals dissolve in the solvent. Use separation techniques, such as chromatography, to separate out mixtures of compounds.
6. The chemicals are made all the time. Raw materials are continuously added and new products are removed.

Sample GCSE questions

1 Use the periodic table in the data sheet to help answer these questions.

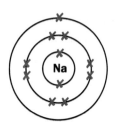

Sodium   Potassium

(a) **(i)** Complete the diagrams to show the electron arrangements of both atoms. **[2]**

> Mark the electrons as clear Xs on the circles. Sodium should have the arrangement 2, 8, 1, while potassium has the arrangement 2, 8, 8, 1. Remember shells fill from the inside outwards.

(ii) Why are sodium and potassium in the same group of the periodic table? **[1]**

Both atoms have the same number of electrons in their outer shells, i.e. one electron.

> Remember that the number of outer shell electrons is the same as the group number.

(iii) Why are sodium and potassium in different periods on the periodic table? **[1]**

Sodium has three shells containing electrons, while potassium has four.

> Remember that the period number is the same as the number of shells the atom has.

(b) Sodium has mass number 23, potassium has mass number 39.

(i) How many protons are in an atom of sodium? **[1]**

11

> Be careful! The number of protons is the same as the number of electrons you drew in part a(i). The mass number is not needed to calculate the number of protons!

(ii) How many neutrons are in an atom of potassium? **[1]**

The number of neutrons is mass number – atomic number: 39 – 19 = 20 neutrons.

(c) Sodium metal reacts with water to produce hydrogen gas and sodium hydroxide:

$2Na(s) + 2H_2O(l) \rightarrow 2NaOH(aq) + H_2(g)$

(i) Which gas would be produced when potassium reacts with water? **[1]**

Hydrogen.

> If you read the question properly, you will notice that it is now asking about potassium, not sodium.

> Elements in the same group have similar reactions, so the gas will be hydrogen again.

Sample GCSE questions

(ii) Give the name and formula of the other product. **[1]**

If sodium produces sodium hydroxide, potassium will produce potassium hydroxide.

The formula for potassium hydroxide is KOH.

❷ **(a)** A company called 'Moreco' wants to manufacture and market a new painkiller based on a compound originally extracted from a rare South American plant. Scientists at Moreco have managed to synthesise a similar compound, which has the same painkilling properties.

(i) Why has Moreco produced a synthetic version of the compound, rather than using the original plant extract?

[2]

Moreco have developed a synthetic alternative so that they are not dependent on such a limited raw material and to keep costs down.

(ii) Why should the Moreco painkiller be thoroughly tested before a licence is given for the company to market their product?

[2]

The product must be safe for humans to take. It must be free from unwanted side-effects.

(iii) Why is it better that the testing of the painkiller is carried out independently, rather than by Moreco's own scientists?

[2]

The scientists working for Moreco may be biased, because Moreco will profit from the licence being given. Independent scientists would not be biased.

(b) Apart from the cost of testing the product, to ensure it is safe for human consumption, what other costs would Moreco have to take into account when deciding the selling price for their new painkiller?

[4]

Any four from:
- *cost of raw materials to make the product*
- *research and development costs in the initial stages*
- *energy costs involved in production*
- *advertising and marketing costs*
- *packaging and distribution costs*

Check the symbol for potassium, using the periodic table, before writing the formula (it is K!)

The formula doesn't need a 2 in front, because you aren't balancing an equation.

Always read the information given: it tells you the plant is 'rare' and that it grows in South America.

When phrasing your answer, you should mention that safety is in relation to human consumption, and that side-effects may otherwise cause problems.

When answering any question where you have to compare two alternatives, always try to comment on both in your answer.

Where you have a lot of space for a number of marks, it is best to bullet-point your answers.

Exam practice questions

1 The nucleus of a neon atom has 10 protons and 10 neutrons.

    (a) What is the atomic number of neon? .... **[1]**

    (b) What is the atomic mass of a neon atom? .... **[1]**

    (c) What is the electron arrangement of a neon atom? .... **[1]**

    (d) Where would you expect to find neon on the periodic table? **[2]**

    ....

    ....

2 The compound, calcium carbonate, has the formula $CaCO_3$.

    (a) How many chemical elements have combined in calcium carbonate?

    .... **[1]**

    (b) How many atoms, in total, are represented by the formula $CaCO_3$?

    .... **[1]**

    (c) A calcium ion has the formula Ca^{2+}: how is it different from a calcium atom?

    .... **[2]**

    (d) What is the charge on a carbonate ion: $CO_3^{?}$?

    .... **[1]**

3 An outline of the modern Periodic Table is shown:

    (a) What is the area that is shaded called? .... **[1]**

    (b) What type of element is found in this region? .... **[1]**

4 **(a)** Write the balanced symbol equation for the following reaction.

               Magnesium + Chlorine ⟶ Magnesium chloride

    .... **[2]**

    (b) Write the balanced symbol equation for the following reaction.

               Iron + Oxygen ⟶ Iron(III) oxide

    .... **[2]**

Exam practice questions

5 The elements of group 7 are called the halogens.

(a) What happens to the melting points of halogens as you go down the group?

.... **[1]**

(b) What happens to the reactivity of halogens as you go down the group?

.... **[1]**

(c) Explain the trend in reactivity in terms of the structure of halogen atoms.

....

.... **[2]**

6 **(a)** Pharmaceutical drugs are made using a batch process.

Explain why the materials needed to make new medicines are expensive.

....

.... **[1]**

(b) Describe the advantages of using a batch process to make a chemical.

....

....

.... **[3]**

7 Magnesium oxide is an ionically bonded compound. It contains magnesium ions: Mg^{2+}, and oxide ions: O^{2-}.

Describe the properties you would expect magnesium oxide to have, making it clear how you are able to make these deductions from the information that is given.

The quality of written communication will be assessed in your answer to this question.

....

....

....

....

....

....

....

....

.... **[6]**

6 Metals, tests and analysis

The following topics are covered in this chapter:

- Metals
- Group 1
- Transition metals
- Chemical tests 1
- Chemical tests 2
- Analysis

6.1 Metals

LEARNING SUMMARY	After studying this section, you should be able to:
	• Describe how metal atoms bond together.
	• Draw and label a diagram to show metallic bondng and structure.
	• Compare the properties of metals with non-metals.
	• Understand the term 'shape-memory alloy'.
	• Explain how a superconductor works.

Metallic structure

AQA	C2	✓
OCR A	C5	✓
OCR B	C4	✓
EDEXCEL	C2	✓

Metals have a giant structure. In metals, the electrons in the highest energy shells (outer electrons) are not bound to one atom but are **delocalised**, or free to move through the whole structure. This means that metals consist of positive metal ions surrounded by a sea of negative electrons. **Metallic bonding** is the attraction between these positive ions and the negative electrons. This is an **electrostatic** attraction.

> Remember, the metallic bond is the electrostatic attraction between the positive metal ions and the delocalised electrons.

Metallic structure

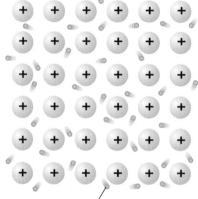

Moving electrons can carry the electric charge or thermal (heat) energy.

Properties of metals

AQA	C2	✓
OCR A	C5	✓
OCR B	C4	✓
EDEXCEL	C2	✓
WJEC	C2	✓

Metallic bonding means that metals have several very useful properties:

- The free electrons mean that metals are **good electrical conductors**.
- The free electrons also mean that metals are **good thermal conductors**.
- The strong attraction between the metal ions and the electrons means that metals can be drawn into wires as the ions slide over each other.
- Metals can also be hammered into shape.
- Most have **high melting points** because lots of energy is needed to overcome the strong metallic bonds.

Remember to say that metals conduct electricity because the delocalised electrons can move. Do not talk about atoms or ions moving.

Non-metals

WJEC	C2	✓

Non-metals are found on the right-hand side of the periodic table. They tend to be **poor electrical and thermal conductors**. Non-metals generally have **low melting points** and boiling points and are sometimes gases at room temperature.

Smart alloys

AQA	C2	✓
WJEC	C2	✓

Smart alloys are new materials with amazing properties. One famous example of a smart alloy is **nitinol**. Nitinol is an alloy of nickel and titanium. Some smart alloys have a shape memory. When a force is applied to a smart alloy it **stretches**. When a smart alloy is heated up, however, it returns to its original shape.

Smart alloys appear to have a **shape memory** because they are able to exist in two solid forms. A temperature change of 10–20 degrees is enough to cause smart alloys to change forms. Shape-memory polymers behave in a similar way, returning to their original shape when heated. At low temperatures, smart alloys exist in their low temperature form.

If a force is applied to the alloy it can be distorted to the low temperature, deformed form of the alloy.

When the alloy is heated, it changes to the higher temperature form.

In shape-memory alloys, the low temperature form and the high temperature form are the same shape and size, so when they are heated smart alloys appear to have a shape memory. Nitinol is used in some dental braces.

Superconductors

OCR B	C4	✓

Some metals can behave as **superconductors** at very low temperatures. Metals can conduct electricity because they have delocalised electrons that can move. Metals normally have a **resistance** to the current that is flowing. Energy is lost as the current overcomes this resistance and the metal warms up.

Superconductors are special because they have **little or no resistance**. The advantages of using superconductors include:

- If there is no resistance then no energy is lost when a current flows.
- As the resistance decreases the current can flow faster, so super-fast circuits can be developed.
- They can be used to make powerful electromagnets.

Despite these advantages, superconductors are not widely used because they only work below a **critical temperature**. Although this varies for different superconductors, the current critical temperatures are around –170°C; until they work at room temperature, their use is likely to be limited.

PROGRESS CHECK

1. What is metallic bonding?
2. Why are metals good electrical conductors?
3. Which metals are used to make nitinol?
4. Why do metals have high melting points?
5. Give a use of nitinol.
6. Why is the use of superconductors limited at present?

1. Metallic bonding is the attraction between the positive metal ions and the sea of negative, delocalised electrons.
2. They have delocalised electrons that can move.
3. Nickel and titanium.
4. A lot of energy is required to overcome the metallic bonds.
5. Nitinol is used in some dental braces.
6. Superconductors only work below their critical temperatures; at present these temperatures are too low to be readily attainable.

6.2 Group 1

LEARNING SUMMARY

After studying this section, you should be able to:

- Recall the characteristic properties of group 1 elements.
- Write equations for reactions between a group 1 element and water.
- Explain why elements in the same group react in a similar way.
- Explain the increase in reactivity as you go down group 1.
- Describe trends in physical properties of group 1 elements.

The group 1 metals

OCR A	C4	✓
OCR B	C4	✓
EDEXCEL	C2	✓
WJEC	C2	✓

The **elements** in group 1, on the far left-hand side of the periodic table, are known as the **alkali metals**. They are soft metals with fairly **low melting points**.

Rubidium and caesium belong to group 1, but are too **reactive** for use in schools. As alkali metals get more reactive they react more vigorously with water. Alkali metals are so reactive that they must be stored under oil to prevent them reacting with moisture or oxygen. Alkali metals are shiny when freshly cut, but they tarnish quickly as they react with oxygen. Gloves and goggles should be worn when using alkali metals.

Alkali metals have **low densities** – lithium, sodium and potassium are all less dense than water. The alkali metals become denser down the group. When alkali metal atoms react they lose the single electron in their outermost shell to form ionic compounds in which the alkali metal ions have a 1+ charge. For example:

$Na \rightarrow Na^+ + e$

> **KEY POINT**
>
> The alkali metals react with water to form strongly **alkaline hydroxide** solutions and hydrogen gas.

metal + water $\rightarrow$ metal hydroxide + hydrogen

To get a top grade, you need to be able to write the symbol equations to sum up these three reactions.

$2Li + 2H_2O \rightarrow 2LiOH + H_2$
$2Na + 2H_2O \rightarrow 2NaOH + H_2$
$2K + 2H_2O \rightarrow 2KOH + H_2$

Metal	Observations when metal reacts with water	Equation
Lithium, Li	Metal floats on water. Some bubbles seen.	Lithium + Water $\rightarrow$ Lithium Hydroxide + Hydrogen
Sodium, Na	Metal forms a molten ball that moves around on the surface of the water. Many bubbles seen.	Sodium + Water $\rightarrow$ Sodium Hydroxide + Hydrogen
Potassium, K	The metal reacts even more vigorously than sodium (it can ignite). Lots of bubbles are seen and the metal burns with a lilac flame.	Potassium + Water $\rightarrow$ Potassium Hydroxide + Hydrogen

Why group 1 metals all react in a similar way

AQA	C2	✓
OCR A	C4	✓
OCR B	C4	✓
WJEC	C2	✓

Alkali metals have just one electron in their outer shell and have similar properties because they have similar electron structures. Alkali metals react with non-metals to form ionic compounds. For example, sodium reacts with chlorine to form sodium chloride.

sodium + chlorine $\rightarrow$ sodium chloride

When sodium is burned, it reacts with oxygen to form sodium oxide.

sodium + oxygen $\rightarrow$ sodium oxide

To get a top grade, you need to be able to write the symbol equations to sum up these reactions.

$2Na + Cl_2 \rightarrow 2NaCl$

$4Na + O_2 \rightarrow 2Na_2O$

When they react, an alkali metal atom loses its outer electron to form ions with a 1+ charge.

$Na \rightarrow Na^+ + e^-$

The alkali metal atom has lost an electron so it is **oxidised**. Alkali metals form solid white ionic compounds that dissolve to form colourless solutions.

The further down the group the further the outer electron is from the nucleus. Further down the group there are more shells shielding the outer electron from the atom's nucleus, so it is easier for atoms to lose their outer electron.

Melting and boiling points of group 1 metals

OCR A   C4   ✓

Melting and boiling points decrease down the group. Alkali metals are held together by metallic bonding. Metallic bonding is the attraction between the positive metal ions and the 'sea' of negative electrons.

The atoms get larger down the group, so the strength of the metallic bonding decreases. As the forces of attraction become weaker down the group it takes less energy to overcome these forces so the alkali metals will melt and boil at lower temperatures.

PROGRESS CHECK

1. Name the first three metals in group 1.
2. How many electrons are present in the outer shell of all group 1 metals?
3. Why do all the group 1 metals have similar properties?
4. What type of compounds do group 1 metals form?
5. Potassium reacts with chlorine to produce the compound potassium chloride.
   a) Write a word and symbol equation to sum up this reaction.
   b) Is the potassium oxidised or reduced in this reaction? Explain your answer.

b) $K \rightarrow K^+ + e^-$. Potassium has lost an electron so it is oxidised in this reaction.

$2K + Cl_2 \rightarrow 2KCl$

5. a) potassium + chlorine → potassium chloride

4. Ionic compounds.

1+.

3. They have the same outer electron structure.

2. One.

1. Lithium, sodium and potassium.

6.3 Transition metals

After studying this section, you should be able to:

- Show where transition metals are found on the Periodic Table.
- Recall the properties of a typical transition metal.
- Relate the properties of transition metals to their uses.
- Describe how copper can be extracted from copper carbonate and from copper oxide.
- Explain the purification of copper by electrolysis.

Properties and reactions of transition metals

OCR B   C4   ✓
EDEXCEL   C2   ✓

Transition metals are found in the middle section of the periodic table. Copper, iron and nickel are examples of very useful transition metals.

> **KEY POINT**
>
> All transition metals have characteristic properties:
>
> - High **melting points** (except for mercury, which is a liquid at room temperature).
> - A high **density**.
>
> There are **coloured compounds**:
>
> - Copper(II) compounds are blue or green.
> - Iron(II) compounds are green.
> - Iron(III) compounds are a 'foxy' red.

Transition metals are also strong, tough, good thermal and electrical conductors, malleable and hard wearing. All transition metals are much less reactive than group 1 metals. They react much less vigorously with oxygen and water. Many transition metals can form ions with different charges. This makes transition metals useful catalysts for many reactions.

Copper and iron

OCR B   C4   ✓

Copper has some very special properties:

- It is a good **thermal** and **electrical conductor**.
- It is easy to shape.
- It is very **unreactive** – even with water.
- It has an attractive colour and lustre.
- It is very resistant to **corrosion**.

Copper's properties mean that it is a very useful metal. Copper is used to make water pipes and tanks, saucepans, and electrical wires.

Iron made in the **blast furnace is strong but brittle**. Iron is often made into steel. **Steel** is strong and cheap and is used in vast quantities, but it is also heavy and may rust. Iron and steel are useful structural materials. They are used to make buildings, bridges, ships, cars and trains. Iron is used as a **catalyst** in the **Haber process**.

Extraction of copper

OCR A   C5   ✓

Copper is an unreactive metal that has several ores. It has been known since ancient times, so the richest supplies of ores have been exhausted. Copper is now extracted from rocks that do not contain large amounts of the metal. This means that a lot of rock has to be **quarried** in order to extract enough copper which can cause significant damage to the local area.

Copper sometimes is found uncombined (or native) in nature. The mineral malachite contains copper carbonate, $CuCO_3$. When it is heated, the copper carbonate breaks down to form copper oxide and carbon dioxide.

copper carbonate → copper oxide + carbon dioxide

$$CuCO_3 \rightarrow CuO + CO_2$$

The copper oxide produced reacts with carbon to form copper and carbon dioxide.

copper oxide + carbon → copper + carbon dioxide

$$2CuO + C \rightarrow 2Cu + CO_2$$

Purification of copper

OCR A   C5   ✓
OCR B   C4   ✓

Copper must be purified before it can be used for some applications, such as high-specification wiring. Copper is purified using electrolysis.

Electrolysis of copper

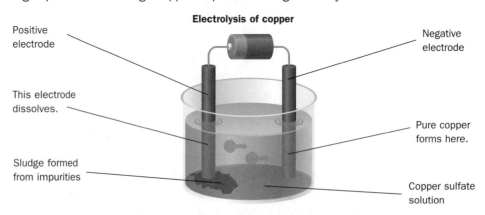

Positive electrode

Negative electrode

This electrode dissolves.

Pure copper forms here.

Sludge formed from impurities

Copper sulfate solution

- During the electrolysis of copper, the impure copper metal is used as the positive electrode where the copper atoms give up electrons to form copper ions.
- As the positive electrode dissolves away, any impurities fall to the bottom of the cell to form sludge.
- Copper ions in the solution are attracted towards the negative electrode where the copper ions gain electrons to form copper atoms.
- The positive electrode gets smaller while the negative electrode gets bigger. In addition, the negative electrode is covered in very pure copper.

PROGRESS CHECK

1 In which section of the periodic table are the transition metals found?
2 Why is copper used for electrical wiring and for water pipes?
3 In which process is iron used as a catalyst?

3. The Haber process.
2. It is a good electrical conductor that can be shaped.
1. The middle section.

6.4 Chemical tests 1

After studying this section, you should be able to:

- Recall the gas tests for carbon dioxide, hydrogen, chlorine, oxygen and ammonia.
- Describe how to carry out a flame test.
- Link the flame test colour to the presence of certain metal ions.
- Link hazard symbols to their meanings.
- Describe the purposes of a number of useful separation techniques.

Gas tests

| OCR B | C4 | ✓ |
| EDEXCEL | C2 | ✓ |

Chemists use these tests to identify the following common gases:

Make sure you are familiar with the tests for common gases – you will need to state the reagents used and the results in the exam.

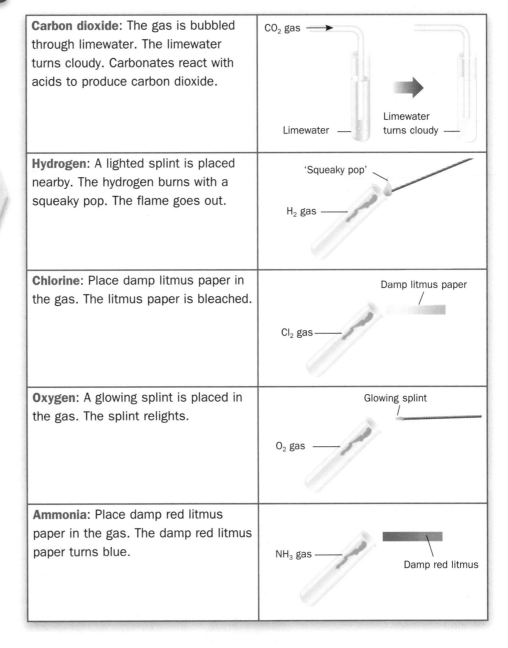

Carbon dioxide: The gas is bubbled through limewater. The limewater turns cloudy. Carbonates react with acids to produce carbon dioxide.	CO$_2$ gas → / Limewater / Limewater turns cloudy
Hydrogen: A lighted splint is placed nearby. The hydrogen burns with a squeaky pop. The flame goes out.	'Squeaky pop' / H$_2$ gas
Chlorine: Place damp litmus paper in the gas. The litmus paper is bleached.	Damp litmus paper / Cl$_2$ gas
Oxygen: A glowing splint is placed in the gas. The splint relights.	Glowing splint / O$_2$ gas
Ammonia: Place damp red litmus paper in the gas. The damp red litmus paper turns blue.	NH$_3$ gas / Damp red litmus

Flame tests

OCR A	C4	✓
OCR B	C4	✓
EDEXCEL	C2	✓
WJEC	C2	✓

Flame tests can be used to identify some metals present in salts. These elements give distinctive flame colours when heated because the light given out by a particular element gives a characteristic **line spectrum**. The technique of **spectroscopy** has been used by scientists to discover new elements, including caesium and rubidium. What do you do?

- Clean a flame test wire by placing it into the hottest part of a Bunsen flame.
- Dip the end of the wire into water and then into the salt sample.
- Hold the salt in the hottest part of the flame and observe the colour seen.

For flame tests, give the name of the metal responsible for a colour, not the name of a whole compound.

Metal ion present	Colour in flame test
Lithium	Crimson
Sodium	Yellow/orange
Potassium	Lilac
Calcium	Red
Barium	Light green
Copper	Blue/green

Hazard symbols

| OCR A | C4, C6 | ✓ |
| EDEXCEL | C2 | ✓ |

Hazard symbols are a very effective way of alerting people to the dangers associated with different chemicals.

Toxic These substances can kill. They can act when you swallow them, breathe them in or absorb them through your skin. *Example: chlorine gas.*		**Corrosive** These substances attack other materials and living tissue, including eyes and skin. *Example: concentrated sulfuric acid.*	
Oxidising These substances provide oxygen, which allows other substances to burn more fiercely. *Example: hydrogen peroxide.*		**Irritant** These substances are not corrosive but they can cause blistering of the skin. *Example: calcium chloride.*	
Harmful These substances are similar to toxic substances but they are less dangerous. *Example: lead oxide.*		**Explosive** These substances are explosive. *Example: urea nitrate.*	
Highly Flammable These substances will catch fire easily. They pose a serious fire risk. *Example: hydrogen.*		Questions are often asked about hazard symbols. Make sure you can identify what each symbol shows and explain what it means.	

Useful techniques in science

OCR A   C6   ✓

- **Dissolving** is used to form a solution from a soluble solute and a suitable solvent.
- **Crystallisation** is used to produce solid crystals from a solution.
- **Filtration** is used to separate an insoluble solid from a mixture.
- **Evaporation** is used to turn a liquid into a gas. If a solution is evaporated to dryness the mass of the solute can be found.
- **Drying**, in an oven or in a desiccator, is used to remove water from a sample.

PROGRESS CHECK

1. What are the tests for carbon dioxide, hydrogen, chlorine and oxygen?
2. Which scientific technique is used to separate an insoluble solid from a mixture?
3. Describe how you would carry out a flame test.

3. First, clean a flame test wire by placing it into the hottest part of a Bunsen flame. Next, dip the end of the wire into water and then into the salt sample. Finally, hold the salt in the hottest part of the flame and observe the colour seen.

2. Filtration.

Oxygen relights a glowing splint.
Chlorine bleaches damp litmus paper.
Hydrogen burns with a squeaky pop.

1. When carbon dioxide is bubbled through limewater it turns the limewater cloudy.

6.5 Chemical tests 2

LEARNING SUMMARY

After studying this section, you should be able to:

- Understand how the formula of an ionic compound can be deduced from the charges of the ions.
- Describe how to carry out a test for halide ions and interpret the test result.
- Describe how to carry out a test for sulfate ions and interpret the test results.
- Describe how carbonates can be identified.
- Describe the use of sodium hydroxide to identify metal ions in solution.

Formulae of ionic compounds

OCR A   C4–C6   ✓
OCR B   C3–C4   ✓
EDEXCEL C2   ✓

Metal ions	Non-metal ions
Sodium, Na^+	Oxide, O^{2-}
Magnesium, Mg^{2+}	Chloride, Cl^-
Calcium, Ca^{2+}	Bromide, Br^-
Potassium, K^+	Hydroxide, OH^-
Iron(II), Fe^{2+}	Nitrate, NO_3^-
Iron(III), Fe^{3+}	Carbonate, CO_3^{2-}
Copper(II), Cu^{2+}	Sulphate, SO_4^{2-}

The compound magnesium oxide contains magnesium, Mg^{2+}, and oxide, O^{2-}, ions. For every one magnesium ion, one oxide ion is required. The overall formula for the compound is MgO.

Testing for halide ions

OCR B	C4	✓
EDEXCEL	C2	✓
WJEC	C2	✓

It is important that a test for a particular ion gives a result that is **unique** to that ion for a positive identification to be made. These tests are very important and are used to check for the presence of chemicals in blood and to check the purity of drinking water.

Identifying halide ions			
Halide ion	**Test**	**Results**	**Ionic half equations**
Chloride, Cl^-	Add dilute nitric acid then **silver nitrate** solution	Chloride ions give a white precipitate of silver chloride.	$Ag^+(aq) + Cl^-(aq) \rightarrow AgCl(s)$
Bromide, Br^-	Add dilute nitric acid then **silver nitrate** solution	Bromide ions give a cream precipitate of silver bromide.	$Ag^+(aq) + Br^-(aq) \rightarrow AgBr(s)$
Iodide, I^-	Add dilute nitric acid then **silver nitrate** solution	Iodide ions give a yellow precipitate of silver iodide.	$Ag^+(aq) + I^-(aq) \rightarrow AgI(s)$

Testing for sulfate ions

| EDEXCEL | C2 | ✓ |

To test for the presence of sulfate ions in solution:

- Add barium chloride solution.
- Then add dilute hydrochloric acid.

A white precipitate of barium sulfate shows that sulfate ions are present in the original solution.

barium chloride + sodium sulfate $\rightarrow$ barium sulfate + sodium chloride

Symbol equation:

$$BaCl_2(aq) + Na_2SO_4(aq) \rightarrow BaSO_4(s) + 2NaCl(aq)$$

Ionic equation:

$$Ba^{2+}(aq) + SO_4^{2-}(aq) \rightarrow BaSO_4(s)$$

Identifying carbonates

| AQA | C2 | ✓ |
| OCR A | C6 | ✓ |

Metal **carbonates** react with dilute hydrochloric acid to form a salt, water and carbon dioxide gas. To prove the gas produced is carbon dioxide, place a drop of limewater (calcium hydroxide $Ca(OH)_2$ solution) on a glass rod. If carbon dioxide is present the limewater turns cloudy.

When copper(II) carbonate is heated it decomposes to form copper(II) oxide and carbon dioxide. This can be identified by a distinctive colour change: copper carbonate is green and copper oxide is black.

copper carbonate + hydrochloric acid → copper chloride + water + carbon dioxide

Symbol equation:

$CuCO_3(s) + 2HCl(aq) \rightarrow CuCl_2(aq) + H_2O(l) + CO_2(g)$

Ionic equation:

$CuCO_3(s) + 2H^+(aq) \rightarrow Cu^{2+}(aq) + H_2O(l) + CO_2(g)$

Hydroxide tests

OCR B   C4   ✓

Dilute **sodium hydroxide** solution can be used to test for the presence of some transition metal ions in solution. The sodium hydroxide solution is added drop-wise to the solution of the transition metal compound. The colour of the precipitate formed is used to identify the transition metal ion.

Transition metal ion	Results
Copper(II), Cu^{2+}	Blue precipitate of copper(II) hydroxide, $Cu(OH)_2$.
Iron(II), Fe^{2+}	Green precipitate of iron(II) hydroxide, $Fe(OH)_2$. This quickly darkens as the Fe^{2+} ions are oxidised to Fe^{3+} ions.

Sodium hydroxide can also be used to identify aluminium and calcium ions in solutions.

Metal ion	Results
Aluminium, Al^{3+}	White precipitate that *does* dissolve in excess sodium hydroxide to form a colourless solution.
Calcium, Ca^{2+}	White precipitate that does *not* dissolve in excess sodium hydroxide.

To test for the presence of **ammonium ions** in a compound, add sodium hydroxide solution and then warm the resulting mixture. Then test for the presence of ammonia gas.

PROGRESS CHECK

1. What is the test for the gas carbon dioxide?
2. What colour is the precipitate formed when copper(II) ions react with hydroxide ions?
3. What colour is the precipitate formed when iron(II) ions react with hydroxide ions?
4. Give the ionic equation for the reaction between copper(II) carbonate and hydrochloric acid.

4. $CuCO_3(s) + 2H^+(aq) \rightarrow Cu^{2+}(aq) + H_2O(l) + CO_2(g)$
3. Green.
2. Blue.
1. It turns limewater cloudy.

6.6 Analysis

LEARNING SUMMARY

After studying this section, you should be able to:

- Explain how chromatography can be used to separate and identify substances.
- Explain how gas chromatography and thin-layer chromatography work.
- Describe the use of atomic spectroscopy and mass spectrometry in analysis.

Modern methods of analysis

AQA   C2   ✓

Compared to the more traditional laboratory methods, modern instrumental methods of analysing chemicals are:

- faster
- more sensitive
- more accurate and require smaller sample sizes.

Uses of chromatography

AQA   C2   ✓
EDEXCEL C2   ✓
WJEC   C2   ✓

Chromatography is used to **separate** out the components of a mixture. It is used to analyse colouring agents in foods, flavourings and drugs. The technique is used in the food industry and by forensic scientists.

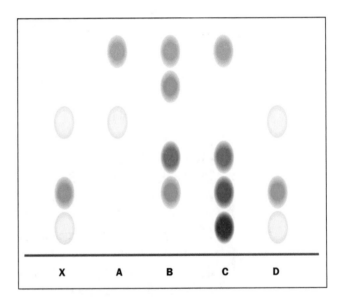

A small spot of the substance being analysed is placed towards the bottom of the chromatography paper. The chromatography paper is then placed into a beaker containing a small amount of the solvent being used. The solvent moves up the paper, carrying the soluble components. When the solvent front reaches the top of the paper, the paper is removed and the solvent is allowed to evaporate. Aqueous solvents contain water and are useful for many ionic compounds. Non-aqueous solvents do not contain water. The more soluble a component is in the solvent the further it will move up the chromatography paper.

R$_f$ values

EDEXCEL C2 ✓
WJEC C2 ✓

The **R$_f$ value** is used to compare the distance the component has moved compared to the distance the solvent front has moved.

$$R_f = \frac{\text{distance moved by the component}}{\text{distance moved by the solvent front}}$$

Determining the R$_f$ value

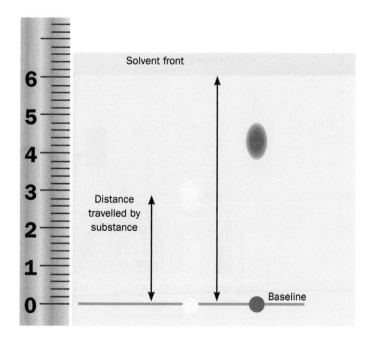

The solvent front has moved 6.0 cm.

The yellow spot has moved 3.2 cm.

The R$_f$ value for the yellow spot = $\frac{3.2\ cm}{6.0\ cm}$ = 0.53

The green spot has moved 4.8 cm.

The R$_f$ value for the green spot = $\frac{4.8\ cm}{6.0\ cm}$ = 0.8

If the same solvent and the same conditions are used, the R$_f$ value would be the same for a given component.

KEY POINT

If the R$_f$ value for an unknown compound is determined it can be identified by comparing this value with the R$_f$ values for known compounds.

Unfortunately, similar compounds often have quite similar R$_f$ values.

Gas chromatography

AQA	C2	✓
WJEC	C2	✓

Gas chromatography is used to identify organic compounds with low boiling points. The retention time is the time that it takes a component to pass through the column of the gas chromatogram. Different components take different times to move through this column and so have different retention times. Unknown compounds can be identified by comparing their retention times with the retention times for known compounds. The areas under the peaks in the chromatogram are proportional to the amount of each compound in the sample. The number of peaks in the chromatogram shows the number of components in the sample.

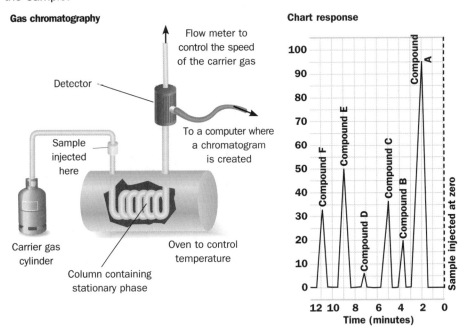

Gas chromatography does have some limitations. Many compounds may have similar retention times, so the peaks for some components may be hidden under the peaks identified for other compounds. Also, it cannot be used to identify new compounds as a reference retention time is required to identify the unknown compound. Gas chromatography is a very reliable technique that is often used as evidence in court cases. It can also be used to test for banned substances in an athlete's blood and for pollutants in air or water samples.

Thin layer chromatography

OCR B	C3	✓

In all types of chromatography, there is a **mobile phase** (the phase that moves) and a **stationary phase** (the phase that does not move). Substances are separated by the movement of the mobile phase through the solid phase. For each component in the mixture there is a dynamic equilibrium between the mobile phase and the solid phase and this is used to separate out the mixture. In **thin layer chromatography** (TLC), the stationary phase is solid and the mobile phase is liquid. This technique is widely used in organic chemistry to check the purity of compounds.

Atomic spectroscopy

WJEC   C2   ✓

Atomic spectroscopy is used to identify the type and concentration of the atoms or ions present in a sample. For example, if a paint sample from a car was found at a crime scene, forensic scientists could use this technique to identify the make and age of the car involved.

Mass spectrometry

AQA   C2   ✓

Mass spectrometry can be used to identify very small samples of material quickly and accurately.

Mass spectrum of ethanol
(C_2H_5OH – relative molecular mass = 46)

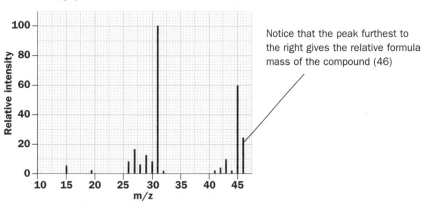

Notice that the peak furthest to the right gives the relative formula mass of the compound (46)

Gas chromatography can be linked to mass spectrometry in a technique known as **GC-MS**. As the sample leaves the gas chromatogram, it is fed into the mass spectrometer and the relative molecular mass of each substance can be identified. The heaviest peak in the sample is known as the molecular ion and can be used to identify the molecular mass of the compound.

PROGRESS CHECK

1. What are the advantages of modern methods of analysis over traditional methods?
2. Why is chromatography useful?
3. Chromatography was used to separate a sample of a food colour containing a blue and a green component. The chromatogram produced showed the solvent front moved 8.0 cm while the green component moved 6.0 cm and the blue component moved 5.0 cm. Calculate the Rf values for the green and blue components.

1. They are faster, more sensitive, more accurate, and smaller samples are needed.
2. It is used to separate out the components of a mixture.
3. Green = $\frac{6.0\ cm}{8.0\ cm}$ = 0.75
   Blue = $\frac{5.0\ cm}{8.0\ cm}$ = 0.625

Sample GCSE questions

1 Rohin had some of a white solid that he knew was a salt of some sort. He decided to analyse the salt to find out what it was.

1

(a) (i) Rohin started his analysis by carrying out a flame test. Describe what he had to do, to carry out this test. **[3]**

He should clean a nichrome wire by dipping it into hydrochloric acid. He should then dip the wire into the salt. He should place the wire in the hottest part of a roaring Bunsen burner flame and should note what colour the flame turned.

(ii) Rohin found that the salt gave a lilac flame. What does this tell him? **[2]**

The salt contains potassium.

The salt is not potassium itself, which is a metal. Learn flame colours!

(b) Rohin took some of the salt and dissolved it in water. He added some nitric acid and then a few drops of silver nitrate solution.

(i) What was Rohin testing for? **[1]**

He was testing to see if the salt was a halide.

Learn these chemical tests!

(ii) If Rohin's test proved negative, which three types of compound can be ruled out? **[3]**

He can rule out chloride, bromide and iodide from the possible identity of the salt.

(c) Rohin added some barium chloride to his salt solution and a white precipitate formed immediately. What is the identity of the salt he was testing? **[1]**

Potassium sulfate.

Note you are being asked for the full name of the salt.

Exam practice questions

1 In metals the outer-shell electrons of the atoms are 'delocalised'.

(a) What does 'delocalised' mean? **[1]**

....

(b) Explain what holds the atoms together in metallic bonding. **[2]**

....

....

(c) What property of metals relies upon the electrons being able to move? **[1]**

....

2 Sodium metal reacts vigorously with water, producing a flammable gas, which sometimes ignites.

(a) Which gas is produced when sodium reacts with water? **[1]**

....

(b) What other product is made in this reaction? **[1]**

....

(c) Write a balanced symbol equation for the reaction. **[2]**

....

3 Flame tests are used in the chemical analysis of salts.

(a) What can be identified by carrying out a flame test? **[1]**

....

(b) If a salt produces a yellow flame, what does that show? **[1]**

....

(c) Why might it be easy to confuse copper salts with barium salts? **[1]**

....

(d) Why must the wire be cleaned before each flame test? **[2]**

....

....

Exam practice questions

4 Testing for the three different halide ions involves adding the same reagent to each, after first acidifying the solution with nitric acid.

(a) What is the reagent used to test for halide ions? **[1]**

....

(b) What result shows a halide is present? **[1]**

....

(c) What is the difference between the result for a chloride and for a bromide? **[2]**

....

....

(d) Write an equation for the reaction between silver ions, Ag^+, and chloride ions, Cl^-. **[1]**

....

5 A customs officer finds a bag of white powder when searching a traveller's rucksack. The traveller tells her it is washing powder. The substance is sent to a forensic laboratory so that it can be analysed using chromatography. The results are shown below.

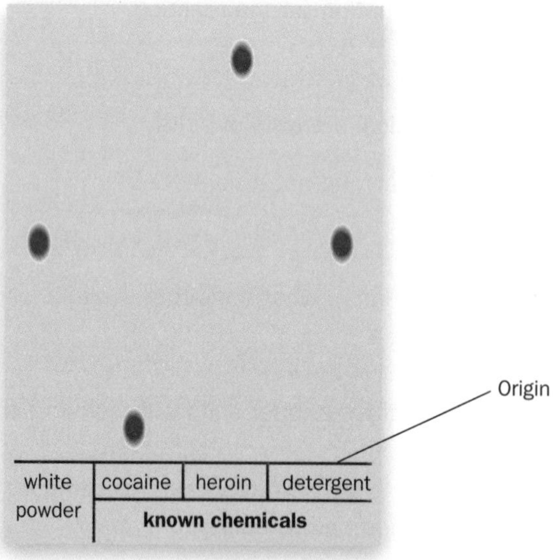

Origin

white powder	cocaine	heroin	detergent
	known chemicals		

(a) Why were samples of cocaine, heroin and detergent tested in addition to the unknown substance? **[1]**

....

(b) Using the chromatogram, state what the unknown white powder is. **[1]**

....

7 Salts and solubility

The following topics are covered in this chapter:

- Making salts
- Metal carbonate reactions
- The electrolysis of sodium chloride
- Water and solubility

7.1 Making salts

LEARNING SUMMARY

After studying this section, you should be able to:

- Use the pH scale as a measure of acidity or alkalinity.
- Explain neutralisation, using the ionic equation for the formation of water.
- Predict what type of salt will be produced when using a given acid.
- Recall that metal salts are made from metals or from metal oxides with acids.
- Understand what is shown by a pH curve for a neutralisation reaction.
- Describe how insoluble salts are prepared by precipitation reactions.

The pH scale

| AQA | C2 | ✓ |
| OCR A | C6 | ✓ |

The pH scale can be used to distinguish between weak and strong acids and alkalis. The pH scale measures the concentration of hydrogen ions. Neutral solutions have a pH of 7. Acidic solutions have a pH of less than 7.

The strongest acids have a pH of 1. Dilute solutions of weak acids have higher pH values than dilute solutions of strong acids. Many foods, such as lemons, contain acids. These foods taste sour. If water is added to an acid it becomes more dilute and less corrosive. Alkaline solutions have a pH of more than 7. The strongest alkalis have a pH of 14. Many cleaning materials contain alkalis. If water is added to an alkali it becomes more dilute and less corrosive.

The pH scale

1 2 3 4 5 6 7 8 9 10 11 12 13 14

ACIDS ← → ALKALIS

Neutralisation reactions

| AQA | C2 | ✓ |
| OCR A | C6 | ✓ |

The reaction between an acid and a base is called **neutralisation**.

- Acidic solutions contain hydrogen, H^+ ions.
- Alkaline solutions contain hydroxide, OH^- ions.

The reaction between an acid and an alkali can be shown in a word equation:

acid + alkali → salt + water

The ionic equation for all neutralisation reactions is:

$H^+(aq) + OH^-(aq) → H_2O(l)$

The type of salt that is produced during the reaction depends on the acid and the alkali used. Indigestion medicines contain chemicals that react with, and neutralise, excess stomach acid.

Naming salts

| AQA | C2 | ✓ |
| OCR A | C6 | ✓ |

Neutralising hydrochloric acid will produce **chloride salts**.

hydrochloric acid + sodium hydroxide → sodium chloride + water

Neutralising nitric acid will produce **nitrate salts**.

nitric acid + potassium hydroxide → potassium nitrate + water

Neutralising sulfuric acid will produce **sulfate** salts.

sulfuric acid + sodium hydroxide → sodium sulfate + water

Ammonia reacts with water to form a weak alkali. Ammonia solution can be neutralised with acids to form **ammonium salts**.

Making salts from metal oxides

| AQA | C2 | ✓ |
| OCR A | C6 | ✓ |

Metal oxides are also bases. They can be reacted with acids to make salts and water:

metal oxide + acid → salt + water

copper(II) oxide + hydrochloric acid → copper(II) chloride + water
Cu + $2HCl$ → $CuCl_2$ + H_2O

zinc oxide + sulfuric acid → zinc sulfate + water
ZnO + H_2SO_4 → $ZnSO_4$ + H_2O

Making salts from metals

| AQA | C2 | ✓ |
| OCR A | C6 | ✓ |

Fairly reactive metals can be reacted with acids to form a salt and hydrogen. Salts of very unreactive metals, such as copper, cannot be made in this way because these metals do not react with acids.

Salts of very reactive metals, such as sodium, cannot be made in this way because the reaction between the metal and acid is too vigorous to be carried out safely.

Precipitation reactions

AQA   C2   ✓
EDEXCEL   C2   ✓

To get a top grade, make sure you can write the symbol equation for this reaction.

$BaCl_2(aq) + Na_2SO_4(aq) \rightarrow BaSO_4(s) + 2NaCl(aq)$

Some **insoluble** salts can be made from the reaction between two solutions. Barium sulfate is an insoluble salt. It can be made by the reaction between solutions of barium chloride and sodium sulfate.

barium chloride + sodium sulfate → barium sulfate + sodium chloride

Precipitation reactions can be used to remove unwanted ions from solutions. This technique is used to treat drinking water and to treat effluent.

> ### PROGRESS CHECK
>
> 1. What is formed when sulfuric acid reacts with sodium hydroxide?
> 2. What is the reaction between an acid and a base called?
> 3. Which ions are found in all acids?
> 4. What sort of salt does nitric acid produce?
> 5. What is produced when acids react with metal oxides?
>
> 5. A salt and water.
> 4. Nitrates.
> 3. Hydrogen, H^+ ions.
> 2. Neutralisation.
> 1. Sodium Sulfate + Water.

7.2 Metal carbonate reactions

LEARNING SUMMARY

After studying this section, you should be able to:

- Write balanced equations for metal carbonate reactions with acids.
- Predict the salt produced when a metal carbonate reacts with a given acid.
- Describe the procedure for making a soluble salt from the reaction between a metal carbonate and acid.

Making salts from metal carbonates

AQA   C2   ✓

Acids can be neutralised by metal carbonates to form salts. Most metal carbonates are insoluble, so they are bases, but they are not alkalis. When acids are neutralised by metal carbonates, a salt, water and carbon dioxide are produced. This means that rocks, such as limestone, that contain metal carbonate compounds are damaged by acid rain. The general equation for the reaction is:

metal carbonate + acid → salt + water + carbon dioxide

A gas (carbon dioxide) is made so bubbles will be seen. The name of the salt produced depends on the acid and the metal carbonate used.

- Hydrochloric acid makes chloride salts.
- Sulfuric acid makes sulfate salts.

- Nitric acid makes nitrate salts.
- Ethanoic acid is neutralised to form ethanoate salts.
- Phosphoric acid is neutralised to form phosphate salts.

The reactions between acids and metal carbonates are exothermic.

Examples of carbonate reactions

| AQA | C2 | ✓ |
| OCR A | C6 | ✓ |

zinc carbonate + sulfuric acid → zinc sulfate + water + carbon dioxide

$ZnCO_3$ $+ H_2SO_4$ → $ZnSO_4$ $+ H_2O$ $+ CO_2$

copper(II) carbonate + hydrochloric acid → copper(II) chloride + water + carbon dioxide

$CuCO_3$ $+ 2HCl$ → $CuCl_2$ $+ H_2O$ $+ CO_2$

Make sure you can apply this idea to other examples.

Making copper chloride

| AQA | C2 | ✓ |
| OCR A | C6 | ✓ |

The diagram below shows how copper chloride salt is made.

Making copper chloride

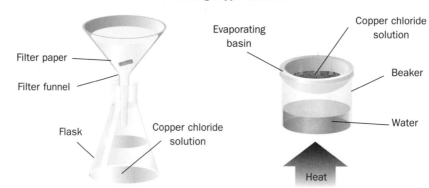

The steps involved in the production of copper chloride are as follows:

1. Copper carbonate is added to hydrochloric acid until all the acid is used up. Solid remains.
2. Any unreacted copper carbonate is filtered off.
3. The solution of copper(II) chloride and water is poured into an evaporating basin.
4. The basin is heated gently until the first crystals of copper chloride start to appear.
5. The solution is then left in a warm place for a few days to allow the remaining copper chloride to crystallise.

PROGRESS CHECK

1. Which gas is given off when metal carbonates react with acids?
2. What sort of salts does hydrochloric acid make?
3. What sort of salts does sulfuric acid make?
4. What sort of salts does nitric acid make?
5. A sample of copper carbonate was reacted with hydrochloric acid. Give the symbol equation for this reaction.

5. $CuCO_3 + 2HCl → CuCl_2 + H_2O + CO_2$
4. Nitrates
3. Sulfates
2. Chlorides
1. Carbon dioxide

7.3 The electrolysis of sodium chloride

<table>
<tr><td rowspan="2">LEARNING SUMMARY</td></tr>
</table>

After studying this section, you should be able to:

- Recall some important uses of sodium chloride.
- Explain the electrolysis of sodium chloride to produce hydrogen, chlorine and sodium hydroxide.
- Write equations for the reactions that occur at the electrodes.
- Recall the main uses of the products of electrolysing sodium chloride solution.
- Understand why the electrolysis of molten sodium chloride has different products.

Sodium chloride

OCR A   C6   ✓

Sodium chloride (**common salt**) is an important resource. It is an **ionic compound** formed from the **combination** of a group 1 metal (sodium) and a group 7 non-metal (chlorine). Sodium chloride is dissolved in large quantities in **seawater**.

Salt can be obtained by **mining** or from allowing seawater to **evaporate**; the method used depends on how the salt is to be used and how pure it needs to be. **Quarrying** salt can have a dramatic impact on the environment. **Rock salt** (unpurified salt) is often used on icy roads. The salt lowers the freezing point of water from 0°C to about −5°C. Sprinkling rock salt on roads means that any water present will not freeze to form ice unless the temperature is very low.

Electrolysis of sodium chloride solution

AQA   C2   ✓
OCR A   C5   ✓
OCR B   C4   ✓

The **electrolysis** of concentrated sodium chloride solution is an important industrial process and produces three useful products (hydrogen, chlorine and sodium hydroxide). The electrodes are made of inert materials so they do not react with the useful products made during the electrolysis reaction.

- During electrolysis, pairs of hydrogen ions, H^+ ions, are attracted to the negative electrode where they pick up electrons to form hydrogen molecules, H_2.

  Hydrogen ions + Electrons → Hydrogen molecules
  $$2H^+ + 2e^- \rightarrow H_2$$

- Pairs of chloride ions, Cl^- ions, are attracted to the positive electrode where they deposit electrons to form chlorine molecules.

  Chloride ions → Chlorine molecules + Electrons
  $$2Cl^- \rightarrow Cl_2 + 2e^-$$

- A solution of sodium hydroxide, $NaOH$ is also produced.

Each of these products (hydrogen, chlorine and sodium hydroxide) can be used to make other useful materials. When there is a mixture of ions, such as Cl⁻ and OH⁻ and Na⁺ and H⁺ as in this case, the products that are formed depends on the **reactivity** of the elements involved. Electrolysis can also be used to **electroplate** objects. This can protect surfaces from **corrosion** and make them more attractive. Copper and silver plating are both produced by electrolysis.

In the electrolysis of a concentration of sodium chloride solution:

* Hydrogen ions are **reduced** to hydrogen molecules; the hydrogen ions both gain an electron to form a hydrogen molecule.
* Chloride ions are **oxidised** to chlorine molecules; the two chloride ions both lose an electron to form a chlorine molecule.

> **KEY POINT**
>
> Reduction and oxidation reactions must always occur together, so they are sometimes referred to as **redox** reactions.

Useful products from the electrolysis of sodium chloride solution

AQA   C2   ✓

Chlorine is used:

* to make **bleach**
* to sterilise water
* to produce hydrochloric acid
* in the production of PVC.

Hydrogen is used in the manufacture of margarine.

Sodium hydroxide is an alkali used in paper making and in the manufacture of many products including soaps and detergents, and rayon and acetate fibres.

Electrolysis of molten sodium chloride

AQA   C2   ✓
OCR A   C5   ✓

Solid sodium chloride does not conduct electricity because the ions cannot move. However, if sodium chloride is heated until it becomes **molten**, the sodium ions and chloride ions can move and electrolysis can occur.

During the electrolysis of molten sodium chloride, the ions move towards the oppositely charged electrodes. Sodium, Na⁺, ions (cations) are attracted to the negative electrode (cathode) where they pick up electrons to form sodium, Na atoms.

Sodium ion + Electron → Sodium atom
$$Na^+ + e^- \rightarrow Na$$

Pairs of chloride ions, Cl⁻, ions (anions) are attracted to the positive electrode (anode) where they deposit electrons to form chlorine molecules.

Chloride ions → Chlorine molecules + Electrons
$$2Cl^- \rightarrow Cl_2 + 2e^-$$

Make sure you can apply these ideas to other examples.

7.4 Water and solubility

Water

OCR A C5 ✓
OCR B C4 ✓
WJEC C2 ✓

The Earth's **hydrosphere** consists of its oceans, seas, lakes and rivers. It consists of water, dissolved salts and gases. Only appropriate sources away from polluted areas are chosen for drinking water. In the UK, water resources are found in lakes, rivers, aquifers (rock formations that contain water) and reservoirs.

Purifying water

OCR B C4 ✓
WJEC C2 ✓

To purify water, first sedimentation is used to settle impurities. Next, the water is filtered to remove solid impurities. Finally, chlorine is added to the water to kill most of the microorganisms in the water. These tiny organisms could multiply quickly and cause disease, so their numbers must be brought down to acceptable levels.

However, some scientists are concerned that even low levels of chlorine in water could cause health problems when the chlorine reacts with organic substances in the water. Some substances may still remain in the water even after purification. These can sometimes be poisonous so scientists regularly check water quality.

In some areas **fluoride** is added to drinking water. This helps to protect children's teeth from decay. However, some people are concerned about adding chemicals to water and about people's right to choose what is best for themselves and their families.

Water pollution

OCR B   C4   ✓

Nitrate fertilisers can cause problems if they are washed into lakes or streams. Water sources can also be polluted by lead compounds from lead pipes and **pesticides** that have been sprayed near to water resources such as reservoirs.

Formula of salts in seawater

OCR A   C5   ✓

As there is no overall charge for the salts in seawater, the charge on the ions can be used to work out the formula of the salt.

Metal ions present in seawater	Non-metal ions present in seawater
Sodium, Na^+	Bromide, Br^-
Potassium, K^+	Chloride, Cl^-
Magnesium, Mg^{2+}	Sulfate, SO_4^{2-}

The compound sodium sulfate contains sodium, Na^+, and sulfate, SO_4^{2-}, ions. For every two sodium ions one sulfate ion is required. The overall formula for the compound is Na_2SO_4.

Solubility

EDEXCEL C2   ✓
WJEC   C2   ✓

Water has many uses including as a coolant, a raw material and as a solvent.

Water is a particularly good **solvent** and dissolves most ionic compounds. The solubility of a substance (called the solute) in water can be measured by measuring the number of grams of the substance that will dissolve in 100 g of water. The more grams of the substance that dissolve the more soluble it is. Generally, the higher the temperature of the water the more soluble a substance will become.

The importance of water

OCR B   C4   ✓
WJEC   C2   ✓

Water is an extremely important resource. The human body consists of about **70% water** and you lose around two and a half litres of water every day. Most of this planet is covered in water, but the vast majority of this water is unsuitable to drink because it is in oceans and seas.

PROGRESS CHECK

1. What is the 'hydrosphere'?
2. Name two chemicals that are sometimes added to our water supplies.
3. What percentage of a human body is water?

3. 70%
2. Chlorine; fluoride.
1. All the waters on the Earth's surface, e.g. oceans, lakes and rivers.

Sample GCSE questions

1 Metal carbonates can be reacted with acids to form salts.

(a) State what type of reaction takes place between a metal carbonate and an acid. **[1]**

A neutralisation reaction.

(b) In addition to a salt, state the two other products of a reaction between a metal carbonate and an acid. **[2]**

Carbon dioxide and water.

(c) What type of salt is formed when hydrochloric acid is reacted with a metal carbonate? **[1]**

A chloride salt

(d) The apparatus shown below is used to produce the salt copper chloride.

Copper carbonate

Hydrochloric acid

With reference to the diagrams, describe the process that is carried out to produce copper chloride crystals.

The quality of written communication will be assessed in this answer. **[6]**

First, an excess of copper carbonate is added to a beaker of hydrochloric acid.

The solution is then filtered to remove any excess copper carbonate. The remaining solution is poured into an evaporating basin, which is gently heated until the first crystals of copper chloride start to appear.

The basin is then left in a warm place for a few days for the remaining copper chloride to crystalise.

Exam practice questions

1   To prepare a sample of copper(II) sulfate, sulfuric acid can be reacted with copper(II) carbonate. To make sure all of the acid has been neutralised, an excess of copper(II) carbonate is used.

    (a)   By what process would any unreacted copper(II) carbonate be removed?   **[1]**

....

    (b)   The copper(II) sulfate produced is a blue solution. How might a solid be obtained?   **[1]**

....

    (c)   Write a word equation for the reaction that takes place.   **[2]**

....

    (d)   Explain why the acid becomes warm as it reacts.   **[1]**

....

2   In the 'Chlor-alkali' industry, a solution called 'brine' is electrolysed to make useful products.

    (a)   What chemical is dissolved in the brine solution?   **[1]**

....

    (b)   In the electrolysis, two gases are produced. What are they?   **[2]**

....

....

    (c)   What is the alkali that gives the industry its name? ....   **[1]**

    (d)   Explain why the electrodes must be chemically inert.   **[1]**

....

3   High levels of nitrates in drinking water have been linked to 'blue baby' syndrome in infants.

    (a)   Explain how nitrates get into drinking water.   **[2]**

....

....

    (b)   Why is it not possible to remove nitrates by filtration?   **[1]**

....

    (c)   Explain why chlorine is added to drinking water.   **[1]**

....

    (d)   Describe how nitrate levels in drinking water can be reduced.   **[1]**

....

Calculation and physical chemistry

The following topics are covered in this chapter:

- **Relative formula mass and percentage composition**
- **Calculations**
- **Rates of reaction**
- **Reversible reactions and the Haber process**
- **Exothermic and endothermic reactions**
- **Explaining energy changes**

8.1 Relative formula mass and percentage composition

LEARNING SUMMARY

After studying this section, you should be able to:

- Recognise the atomic number and the mass number for an element on the periodic table.
- Work out the relative formula mass of a compound from the mass numbers of its elements.
- Calculate the number of moles of an element in a given mass.
- Calculate the number of moles of a compound in a given mass.
- Calculate the percentage by mass of one element in a compound.

Why relative atomic mass is used

AQA	C2	✓
OCR A	C5, C6	✓
OCR B	C3	✓
EDEXCEL	C2	✓
WJEC	C2	✓

The **relative atomic mass** (**RAM** or A_r) is used to compare the masses of different atoms.

> **KEY POINT**
>
> The relative atomic mass of an element is the average mass of one atom of its **isotopes** compared with an atom of carbon-12.

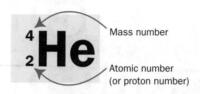

Mass number

Atomic number
(or proton number)

Relative formula mass

AQA	**C2**	✓
OCR A	**C5, C6**	✓
OCR B	**C3**	✓
EDEXCEL	**C2**	✓
WJEC	**C2**	✓

> **KEY POINT**
>
> The **relative formula mass (RFM** or M_r) of a substance is worked out by adding together the relative atomic masses of all the atoms in the ratio indicated by the formula.

Example: For nitrogen, N_2:

$$N_2$$
$$(2 \times 14) = 28$$

The relative formula mass of N_2 is 28. Nitrogen molecules contain a triple covalent bond, which is very strong. This makes nitrogen molecules very stable.

Example: For carbon dioxide, CO_2:

$$CO_2$$
$$12 + (2 \times 16) = 44$$

The relative formula mass of CO_2 is 44.

Example: For water, H_2O:

$$H_2O$$
$$(2 \times 1) + 16 = 18$$

The relative formula mass of H_2O is 18.

Moles

AQA	**C2**	✓

The relative formula mass of a substance in grams is known as 1 **mole** of the substance. This is also known as the molar mass. The units for molar mass are **g/mol**. 1 mole of CO_2 is 44 g and 1 mole of H_2O is 18 g. The number of moles of a substance present can be calculated using the formula below.

$$\text{Number of moles} = \frac{\text{mass of sample}}{\text{relative formula mass of the substance}}$$

Calculations using moles

AQA	C2	✓
OCR B	C3	✓
WJEC	C2	✓

The relative formula mass of water is 18 so the molar mass is 18 g.

$$\text{Number of moles} = \frac{9}{18} = 0.5$$

There are 0.5 moles in 9 g of water.

Example: What is the mass of 0.5 moles of nitrogen?

The relative formula mass of nitrogen is 28.

$$\frac{\text{Mass of}}{\text{sample}} = \frac{\text{number}}{\text{of moles}} \times \frac{\text{relative formula}}{\text{mass of the substance}} = 0.5 \times 28 = 14\ \text{g}$$

The mass of 0.5 moles of nitrogen is 14 g.

Compounds consist of atoms of two or more different elements that have been chemically joined together. The percentage composition of an element in the compound can be calculated using the formula below.

$$\textbf{Percentage mass of an element in a compound} = \frac{\textbf{relative atomic mass} \times \textbf{no. of atoms}}{\textbf{relative formula mass}} \times \textbf{100\%}$$

Example: Ammonium nitrate is used as a fertiliser. Plants absorb fertiliser through their roots, so fertilisers must be soluble. Find the percentage composition of nitrogen in this compound.

- RAM of N = 14
- RAM of H = 1
- RAM of O = 16
- RAM of S = 32

The formula mass of ammonium nitrate, NH_4NO_3 is:

$$NH_4\ NO_3$$

$$14 + (4 \times 1) + 14 + (3 \times 16) = 80$$

The percentage of nitrogen in ammonium nitrate is 35%,

since $\dfrac{2 \times 14}{80} \times 100\% = 35\%$

Example: Ammonium sulfate is also used as a fertiliser. Find the percentage of nitrogen in this compound.

$$(NH_4)_2\ SO_4$$

$$[(14 + (4 \times 1)] \times 2 + 32 + (4 \times 16)$$

The percentage of nitrogen in ammonium sulfate is 21.2%,

since $\dfrac{2 \times 14}{132} \times 100\% = 21.2\%$

1. Why is relative atomic mass used in science?
2. How is the relative formula mass of a substance calculated?
3. What is the relative formula mass of a substance in grams known as?
4. What is the mass of 1 mole of H_2O?
5. **a)** Find the relative formula mass of a nitrogen molecule, N_2.
   b) Find the relative formula mass of carbon dioxide, CO_2.

1. It is used to compare the masses of different atoms.
2. By adding together the relative atomic masses of all the atoms in the ratio indicated by the formula.
3. Molar mass.
4. 18 g.
5. a) 28 g.
   b) 44 g.

8.2 Calculations

LEARNING SUMMARY

After studying this section, you should be able to:

- Calculate the number of moles in a given mass of a substance.
- Calculate the mass in grams, of a given number of moles of a substance.
- Use a balanced equation to relate the number of moles of one substance to the number of moles of another.
- Understand how percentage yield is calculated.
- Understand the term 'atom economy' and know how to calculate it for a given reaction.
- Find the empirical formula of a compound.

Calculating the mass of products

AQA	C2	✓
OCR A	C6	✓
OCR B	C3	✓
EDEXCEL	C2	✓
WJEC	C2	✓

The masses of **products** and **reactants** can be worked out using the **balanced equation** for the reaction.

Example: What mass of water is produced when 8 g of hydrogen is burned?
Relative atomic mass:

H = 1, O = 16

First, write down what happens during the reaction as a word equation.

hydrogen + oxygen → water

Then write it as a balanced symbol equation.

$2H_2 + O_2 \rightarrow 2H_2O$

Next, calculate the **relative formula mass** of a hydrogen molecule and a water molecule.

The relative formula mass of hydrogen, H_2:

$$H_2$$
$$2 \times 1 = 2$$

The relative formula mass of water, H_2O:

$$H_2O$$

$$(2 \times 1) + 16 = 18$$

It is now possible to calculate the number of moles in 8 g of hydrogen.

$$\frac{8}{2} = 4 \text{ moles}$$

Next, examine the balanced symbol equation. Every 2 moles of hydrogen makes 2 moles of water. This means 4 moles of hydrogen will produce 4 moles of water.

Finally, work out the mass of 4 moles of water by rearranging the moles equation.

Mass of sample = number of moles × relative formula mass

$$= 4 \times 18$$
$$= 72$$

This shows that if 8 g of hydrogen is burned completely, 72 g of water vapour will be produced.

Calculating the mass of reactants

AQA	C2	✓
OCR A	C6	✓
OCR B	C3	✓
EDEXCEL	C2	✓
WJEC	C2	✓

The equation for a reaction can also be used to calculate how much of the reactants should be used to produce a given amount of the product.

Example: What mass of magnesium should be used to produce 60 g of magnesium oxide?

Relative atomic mass:

Mg = 24   O = 16

First, write down what happens during the reaction as a word equation.

magnesium + oxygen → magnesium oxide

Then write it as a balanced symbol equation.

$2Mg + O_2 \rightarrow 2MgO$

Next, calculate the relative formula mass of magnesium oxide.

The relative formula mass of magnesium oxide, MgO:

$$MgO$$

$$24 + 16 = 40$$

The relative atomic mass of magnesium is given as 24. It is now possible to calculate the number of moles in 60 g of magnesium oxide.

$$\frac{60}{40} = 1.5 \text{ moles}$$

Next, examine the balanced symbol equation. To make 2 moles of magnesium oxide, 2 moles of magnesium are needed. So, to make 1.5 moles of magnesium oxide, 1.5 moles of magnesium are needed.

Finally, work out the mass of 1.5 moles of magnesium oxide by rearranging the moles equation.

Mass of sample = number of moles × relative formula mass

$$= 1.5 \times 24$$
$$= 36$$

This shows that to make 60 g of magnesium oxide, 36 g of magnesium should be burned.

Percentage yield

AQA	C2	✓
OCR A	C6	✓
OCR B	C3	✓
EDEXCEL	C2	✓
WJEC	C2	✓

The amount of product made in a reaction is called the **yield**. Although atoms are never gained or lost during a chemical reaction, the yield of a reaction is often less than the yield predicted. This can be for a number of reasons:

- The reaction is **reversible** and does not go to completion.
- Some of the product is lost during **filtering**, **evaporation**, when transferring liquids or during **heating**.
- There may be **side-reactions** occurring that produce other products.

The amount of product actually made compared with the maximum calculated yield is called the **percentage yield**. A 100% yield means no product has been lost; a 0% yield means no product has been made.

> **KEY POINT**
>
> $$\text{Percentage yield} = \frac{\text{mass of product}}{\text{maximum calculated yield}} \times 100\%$$

Scientists try to choose reactions with either a high percentage yield or **high atom economy**. This contributes towards **sustainable development** by reducing waste. A 100% atom economy means that all the reactant atoms have been made into the desired products.

Making ethanol

| OCR B | C3 | ✓ |

Ethanol can be made by two different methods. These different methods have very different atom economies. When ethanol is made by reacting ethene with steam, the process has an atom economy of 100%.

$$C_2H_4 + H_2O \rightarrow C_2H_5OH$$

When ethanol is made by fermentation, the atom economy is less.

$$C_6H_{12}O_6 \rightarrow 2C_2H_5OH + 2CO_2$$

$$\text{Atom economy} = \frac{M_r \text{ of desired products}}{M_r \text{ of all products}} \times 100\%$$

$$= \frac{92}{180} = 51.1\%$$

Waste products are undesirable as they cannot always be sold for profit, their disposal can be costly and cause environmental and social problems.

Finding the empirical formula

AQA   C2   ✓
EDEXCEL C2   ✓

KEY POINT

The **empirical formula** of a compound is the ratio of each kind of atom in its simplest form.

Example: Find the empirical formula of magnesium oxide formed when 12 g of magnesium reacts with 8 g of oxygen atoms. Deal with the magnesium and oxygen separately.

	Mg	O
State the number of grams that combine.	12	8
Change the grams to moles (divide by A_r).	$\frac{1}{2}$	$\frac{1}{2}$
This is the ratio in which the atoms combine.	0.5	0.5
Get the ratio into its simplest form.	1	1

The simplest ratio of magnesium atoms to oxygen atoms is 1 : 1 so the empirical formula is MgO.

PROGRESS CHECK

1 What mass of water vapour is produced when 4 g of hydrogen is burned?
2 What mass of water vapour is produced when 16 g of hydrogen is burned?
3 Consider the equation below.
$CaCO_3 \rightarrow CaO + CO_2$
If 5.0 g is heated fiercely, what mass of calcium oxide is produced?

3. 2.8 g.
2. 144 g.
1. 36 g.

8.3 Rates of reaction

LEARNING SUMMARY

After studying this section, you should be able to:

• Describe what is meant by the rate of reaction and how it can be measured.
• Understand the effect of changing the temperature on the rate of a reaction.
• Understand the effect of increasing the surface area on the rate of a reaction.
• Understand the effect of changing concentrations on the rate of a reaction.
• Recall that a catalyst increases the rate of reaction without being used up.

Slow and fast reactions

AQA	C2	✓
OCR A	C6	✓
OCR B	C3	✓
EDEXCEL	C2	✓

The **rate of reaction** is equal to either:

- the amount of reactant used up divided by the time taken, or
- the amount of product made divided by the time taken.

Rusting is an example of a reaction that happens very slowly, while **combustion** reactions and explosions happen very quickly. **Explosions** produce a large volume of **gaseous products**. Factories that produce fine powders, such as custard powder, have to be very careful to prevent explosions from occurring.

Measuring rates of reaction

AQA	C2	✓
OCR A	C6	✓
OCR B	C3	✓
EDEXCEL	C2	✓
WJEC	C2	✓

The method chosen to follow the rate for a particular reaction depends on the reactants and products involved. When sodium thiosulfate reacts with hydrochloric acid, one of the products is a precipitate of sulfur. The rate of reaction can be followed using a light sensor and a data logger to measure how quickly sulfur is being made. A chemical reaction can only occur if the reacting particles collide with enough energy to react. This is called the **activation energy**. If the particles collide but do not have the minimum energy to react, the particles just bounce apart without reacting.

Measuring the rate of reaction

Gas syringe

Dilute
hydrochloric acid

Magnesium

The rate of a chemical reaction can be measured by:

- How fast the products are being made.
- How fast the reactants are being used up.

The graph below shows the amount of product made in two experiments. The lines are steepest at the start of the reaction in both experiments. The lines start to level out as the reactants get used up. When the line becomes horizontal the reaction has finished. The graph shows that experiment 2 has a faster rate of reaction than experiment 1. However, both experiments produce the same amount of product.

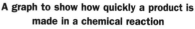

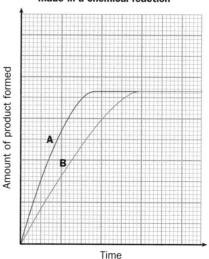

A graph to show how quickly a product is made in a chemical reaction

When analysing graphs, the reaction is over when the graph levels out. Reactions stop when one of the reactants is all used up; this reactant is called the **limiting reactant**. The other reactants may not be completely used up and are said to be in **excess**. The amount of product made depends on the amount of reactant used up; the amount of product made is directly proportional to the amount of reactant used. The rate of reaction is measured using units of g/s or g/min or cm^3/s or cm^3/min.

Temperature

If the temperature Is increased, the reactant particles move more quickly.

> **KEY POINT**
>
> Increasing the temperature increases the rate of reaction because:
>
> * The particles collide more often.
> * When the particles collide, the collisions have more energy.

Increasing the surface area

> **KEY POINT**
>
> For a reaction to occur, the particles have to **collide**. The greater the surface area the more chance of the reactant particles colliding and the faster the rate of reaction.

With a small surface area (large pieces) the rate of reaction is slow. The particles collide less often. With a large surface area (small pieces) the rate of reaction is higher. The particles collide more often.

Remember, small pieces have a large surface area. The dust caused by fine powders, such as custard powder or flour, can burn explosively because of the large surface area of its particles.

Catalysts

A **catalyst** increases the rate of reaction, but is not itself used up during the reaction. Only a small amount of catalyst is needed to catalyse a large amount of reactants. Catalysts are specific to certain reactions. Catalysts offer an alternative reaction pathway with a **lower activation energy**.

Remember, catalysts do not get used up in reactions. Reactions stop when one of the reactants is all used up.

Concentration and pressure

For a reaction to take place, the reactant particles have to collide. If the concentration is increased there are more reactant particles in the solution. Increasing the concentration increases the rate of reaction because the particles collide more often.

For gases, increasing the pressure has the same effect as increasing the concentration of dissolved particles in solutions. At low concentration the rate of reaction slows down because the particles collide less often. At higher concentration the rate of reaction speeds up because the particles collide more often.

PROGRESS CHECK

1. What happens to the rate of reaction if the concentration of reactants is increased?
2. What happens to the rate of reaction if the pressure of gaseous reactants is increased?
3. How does a catalyst affect the rate of reaction?
4. Explain two ways in which increasing the temperature increases the rate of a chemical reaction.

1. It increases.
2. It increases.
3. A catalyst increases the rate of reaction without being used up itself.
4. If the temperature is increased the particles move more quickly. This means the particles collide more often and, when they do collide, the collisions have more energy. As more collisions have a level of energy greater than the activation energy, the particles react more quickly.

8.4 Reversible reactions and the Haber process

After studying this section, you should be able to:

- Recognise that the symbol ⇌ shows a reaction is reversible.
- Understand that a reaction that is exothermic in one direction is endothermic in the other direction.
- Write a balanced equation for the reaction between nitrogen and hydrogen to produce ammonia.
- Describe how the conditions for ammonia production are chosen.
- Understand the role of the iron catalyst in keeping costs down.

Simple reversible reactions

AQA   C2   ✓

In science, not all reactions go to completion.

> **KEY POINT**
>
> Many chemical reactions are **reversible**; they can proceed both forwards and backwards.

If A and B are reactants and C and D are products, a reversible reaction can be summed up as:

A + B ⇌ C + D

The two reactants, A and B, can react to make the products C and D; at the same time, C and D can react together to produce A and B.

Exothermic and endothermic reactions

AQA   C2   ✓
OCR B   C3   ✓

If the forwards reaction is **exothermic** (gives out energy), then the backwards reaction is **endothermic** (takes in energy). The amount of energy given out by the forwards reaction must be the same as the amount of energy taken in by the backwards reaction.

Example: copper(II) sulfate reactions

First, the **hydrated** (with water) copper sulfate is heated to make **anhydrous** (without water) copper sulfate. Then water is added to the anhydrous copper sulfate to produce hydrated copper sulfate.

Copper(II) sulfate reactions

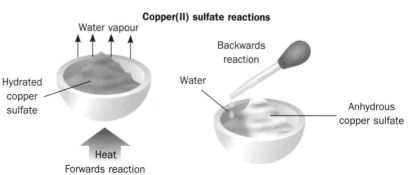

Water vapour

Hydrated copper sulfate

Backwards reaction

Water

Anhydrous copper sulfate

Heat
Forwards reaction

In the forwards reaction, the hydrated copper sulfate takes in energy as it is heated. This is an endothermic reaction.

hydrated copper(II) sulfate (blue) → anhydrous copper(II) sulfate (white) + water

In the backwards reaction, energy is given out when water is added to the anhydrous copper sulfate. This is an exothermic reaction.

anhydrous copper(II) sulfate (white) + water → hydrated copper(II) sulfate (blue)

The Haber process

EDEXCEL C2 ✓

Ammonia is produced by the **Haber process** and is made from **nitrogen** and **hydrogen**.

> **KEY POINT**
>
> Hydrogen is obtained from natural gas or from the **cracking** of oil fractions. Nitrogen is obtained from the **fractional distillation** of liquid air. This is an example of a **reversible reaction**.

$N_2(g) + 3H_2(g) \rightleftharpoons 2NH_3(g)$

Some of the nitrogen and the hydrogen react to form ammonia. At the same time, some of the ammonia breaks down into nitrogen and hydrogen.

The cost of producing ammonia depends on:

- The cost of the raw materials.
- Energy costs.
- Equipment costs.
- Labour costs – the more automation the lower the wages bill will be.
- How quickly the ammonia is produced.

Choosing the conditions for the Haber process

EDEXCEL C2 ✓

> **KEY POINT**
>
> The industrial conditions are specially chosen. Typical conditions are:
>
> - A high pressure (200 atmospheres).
> - A moderate temperature (450°C).
> - An iron **catalyst**.

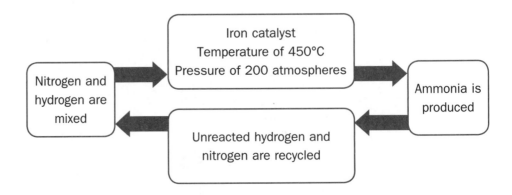

A **high pressure** is used to increase the amount of ammonia produced. In the balanced symbol equation, there are four gas molecules on the left-hand side of the equation (one nitrogen molecule and three hydrogen molecules), but there are only two ammonia molecules on the right-hand side of the equation. Increasing the pressure encourages the forwards reaction, which increases the amount of ammonia produced because there are fewer gas molecules on the right-hand side of the equation. Ideally, the highest possible pressures should be used. However, in practice, it is too expensive to build a plant that can withstand pressures greater than 200 atmospheres.

The reaction between nitrogen and hydrogen to produce ammonia is **exothermic**. A low temperature would increase the **yield** of ammonia produced at equilibrium. It would, however, also make the rate of the reaction very slow. A higher temperature would give a much faster rate of reaction. The yield of ammonia at **equilibrium**, however, would be much lower. In practice, a compromise temperature of 450°C is used. This gives a reasonable yield of ammonia reasonably quickly.

> To get a top grade, you need to explain the conditions used in the Haber process. In the Haber process it is not enough just to state that compromise conditions are used. You should explain why it is a compromise in terms of the rate of reaction and the yield of ammonia.

PROGRESS CHECK

1. What is special about a reversible reaction?
2. What does the Haber process produce?
3. From where are the hydrogen and nitrogen obtained?
4. Why could this reaction be described as reversible?
5. Explain how ammonia can be made into ammonium nitrate. Include symbol equations to sum up each step in the production of this fertiliser.

1. It can proceed in either direction.
2. Ammonia.
3. Hydrogen is obtained from natural gas or the cracking of oil fractions. Nitrogen is obtained from the fractional distillation of liquid air.
4. The reaction can go forwards or backwards.
5. React the ammonia with oxygen in the air over a platinum catalyst.
$$4NH_3 + 5O_2 \rightarrow 4NO + 6H_2O$$
Allow the nitrogen oxide to cool, and then react it with water and more oxygen to form nitric acid.
$$4NO + 3O_2 + 2H_2O \rightarrow 4HNO_3$$
Then react the nitric acid with more ammonia to form ammonium nitrate.
$$HNO_3 + NH_3 \rightarrow NH_4NO_3$$

8.5 Exothermic and endothermic reactions

LEARNING SUMMARY	After studying this section, you should be able to:
	• Understand the terms 'exothermic' and 'endothermic', applied to chemical reactions.
	• Recall that bond breaking is always endothermic and bond making exothermic.
	• Calculate energy changes from the bond energies of bonds broken and made.
	• Interpret energy level diagrams for exothermic and endothermic reactions.

Energy changes and chemical reactions

AQA	C2	✓
OCR A	C6	✓
OCR B	C3	✓
EDEXCEL	C2	✓
WJEC	C2	✓

During chemical reactions atoms are rearranged as old **bonds** are broken and new bonds are made.

KEY POINT

Energy is required to break bonds and is released when new bonds are formed.

If, overall, energy is given to the surroundings, the reaction is described as **exothermic**. If, overall, energy is taken from the surroundings, the reaction is described as **endothermic**.

To work out whether a reaction is endothermic or exothermic, scientists take the temperature of the chemicals before the reaction and then after the reaction. If the temperature has increased the reaction is exothermic; if the temperature has decreased the reaction is endothermic.

Burning methane is an example of an **exothermic reaction**. Rusting, explosions and neutralisation reactions are also exothermic. Self-heating cans and hand warmers make use of exothermic reactions.

The **thermal decomposition** of limestone is an example of an **endothermic reaction**. Photosynthesis and dissolving ammonium nitrate in water are also endothermic reactions. Some sports injury packs make use of endothermic reactions to cool wounds.

Bond energy calculations

EDEXCEL C2 ✓
WJEC C2 ✓

Each chemical bond has a specific **bond energy**. This is the amount of energy that must be taken in to break 1 mole of bonds.

Bond	Bond energy (kJ mol^{-1})
C–H	413
O=O	496
C=O	743
O–H	463
C–O	358

Example: Burning the fuel methane, CH_4.

$$H-\underset{\displaystyle H}{\overset{\displaystyle H}{C}}-H \;+\; \begin{matrix} O=O \\ O=O \end{matrix} \;\rightarrow\; O=C=O \;+\; \begin{matrix} H\diagup{}^{O}\diagdown H \\ H\diagup{}_{O}\diagdown H \end{matrix}$$

Energy taken in to break the bonds:

- 4 moles of C–H = 4 × 413 = 1652 kJ mol^{-1}
- 2 moles of O=O = 2 × 496 = 992 kJ mol^{-1}
- Total = 1652 + 992 = 2644 kJ mol^{-1}

Energy taken in has a positive sign (endothermic).

Energy given out when forming bonds:

- 2 moles of C=O = 2 × 743 = 1486 kJ mol^{-1}
- 4 moles of O–H = 4 × 463 = 1852 kJ mol^{-1}
- Total = 1486 + 1852 = 3338 kJ mol^{-1}

Energy given out has a negative sign (exothermic).

Difference in energy between energy given out and the energy taken in:

= +2644 kJ mol^{-1} – 3338 kJ mol^{-1}

= −694 kJ mol^{-1}

This reaction gives out more energy than it takes in so it is exothermic. The burning of fuels is always exothermic.

Energy level diagrams

OCR A   C6   ✓
EDEXCEL C2   ✓
WJEC   C2   ✓

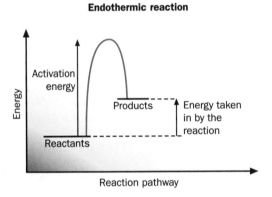

Exothermic reaction

In an exothermic reaction, the products have less energy than the reactants. The difference in energy between the products and the reactants is the amount of energy given out by the reaction.

Endothermic reaction

In an endothermic reaction, the products have more energy than the reactants. The difference in energy between the products and the reactants is the amount of energy taken in by the reaction.

Activation energy

WJEC   C2   ✓

> **KEY POINT**
>
> The **activation energy** is the minimum amount of energy needed to get the **reaction** started. This energy is needed to break the bonds in the reactants. Catalysts provide an alternative reaction pathway that has lower activation energy.

It is very important that scientists continue to develop better **catalysts** that lower activation energies. By using a catalyst, it is possible to increase the rate of reaction. This means lower temperatures and pressures can be used, which has economic benefits, because it costs less, and environmental benefits, as high temperatures and pressures are often obtained by using electricity generated at power stations that burn fossil fuels. If less fossil fuel is being burned then less carbon dioxide is being released into the atmosphere. Using better catalysts also helps to preserve raw materials.

1. The temperature increases during a chemical reaction. What sort of reaction has taken place?
2. How do you know that burning coal is an exothermic reaction?
3. When hydrochloric acid neutralises sodium hydroxide the temperature increases. Is this an exothermic reaction or an endothermic reaction?
4. Sketch an energy level diagram for the combustion of methane.

1. Exothermic.
2. It releases lots of energy.
3. Exothermic.
4. The vertical axis should be labelled 'energy' and the horizontal axis should be labelled 'time', or 'reaction pathway'. The reactants should be labelled as methane and oxygen and should be higher than the products, which should be labelled as carbon dioxide and water. The energy change and the activation energy should also be marked.

8.6 Explaining energy changes

LEARNING SUMMARY

After studying this section, you should be able to:

- Describe how the energy change of a reaction can be measured using calorimetry.
- Recall that the temperature increase in a volume of water can be converted to an energy charge.
- Understand the term 'specific heat capacity' and recall how this is used in the calculation.
- Recognise that heat energy produced can be in kJ/mol, kJ/g or calories/g.
- Recall that burning fuels, displacement reactions and neutralisation reactions are usually exothermic.

Calorimetry

OCR B   C3   ✓

In **exothermic** reactions, more energy is given out when new bonds are formed than when the bonds were broken. In **endothermic** reactions, more energy is taken in to break bonds than is released when new bonds are formed.

Scientists use **calorimetry** to compare the amount of energy released when fuels and foods are burned. A fixed amount of water is placed into a boiling tube and its temperature is taken using a thermometer.

Calorimetry

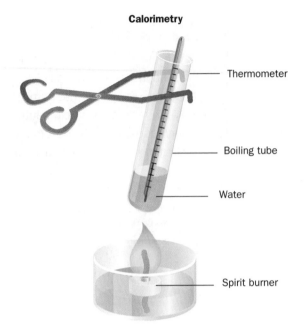

The sample is then burned under the boiling tube containing the water, and the water is gradually warmed up. The temperature of the water is taken at the end of the experiment.

To compare the energy transferred when liquid fuels are burned, place the fuel in a **spirit burner**. Find the mass of the spirit burner and the fuel. Use the spirit burner to heat the water, then find the new mass of the remaining fuel and the spirit burner. The amount of fuel used is the difference between the mass at the start and at the end.

The chemical energy that had been stored in the sample is released as thermal energy when the sample is burned. The greater the change in temperature of the water the more energy was stored in the fuel.

A displacement reaction

| OCR B | C3 | ✓ |
| EDEXCEL | C2 | ✓ |

Calorimetry experiments can be used to work out the energy released by chemical reactions in solution. In the example below, a more reactive metal, iron, displaces a less reactive metal, copper from a solution of copper sulfate.

Measuring the temperature change of a displacement reaction

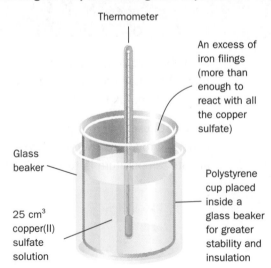

Temperature at the start of the reaction.	15°C
Temperature at the end of the reaction.	33°C
Change in temperature.	18°C

The specific heat capacity of copper(II) sulfate solution = 4.2 J/g/°C.

Calculating the energy change

OCR B   C3   ✓

Calorimetry can also be used to measure the energy change when solids **dissolve** in water and in **neutralisation** reactions.

The reaction above is carried out inside an insulated container, such as a polystyrene cup. The temperature of the solution is taken at the start and end of the experiment to work out the change in temperature. As 1 cm^3 of solution is assumed to have a mass of 1 g, a mass of 25 g is used for the mass of the solution.

Energy change = mass × specific heat capacity × change in temperature
= 25 g × 4.2 J/g/°C × 18°C
= 1890 J or 1.890 kJ

PROGRESS CHECK

1. What happens in chemical reactions?
2. Name the piece of apparatus used to measure temperature.
3. What sort of energy is stored in food and fuels?
4. What sort of energy is released when food and fuels are burned?

4. Thermal energy.
3. Chemical energy.
2. A thermometer.
1. Bonds are broken and new bonds are formed.

Sample GCSE questions

1   The graph, below, follows the volume of carbon dioxide released by the reaction between excess calcium carbonate, in the form of marble chips, and hydrochloric acid solution over time.

$$CaCO_3(s) + 2HCl(aq) \rightarrow CaCl_2(aq) + CO_2(g) + H_2O(l)$$

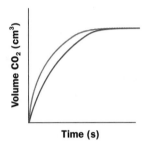

(a) (i)   What feature of the graph shows the rate of the reaction? **[1]**

The gradient of this type of graph shows the rate of reaction.

(ii)   Describe what happens to the rate of this reaction over the period of time shown.   **[2]**

The rate is high at the start, but gradually decreases to zero.   ← Remember you are commenting on the gradient, not the volume of CO_2.

(iii)   Use the collision theory to explain the change in rate you have described.   **[2]**

As the acid reacts, the number of particles of acid falls, meaning that collisions between acid particles and the marble become fewer.

(b) (i)   Draw a second line on the graph, showing what you would expect if the same volume of acid had been diluted with an equal volume of water before adding it to the marble chips.   **[2]**   ← The second line should be less steep at the start, but it should follow the same shape of curve and end up at exactly the same volume of CO_2.

(ii)   Explain why the second line, that you have added, is different to the first.   **[2]**

It is less steep at the start because there is a lower concentration of acid. Fewer particles of acid (per cm^3) will result in fewer collisions.

(iii)   Comment on the total volume of CO_2 produced in both experiments.   **[2]**

Although the acid is diluted in the second experiment, there is still the same amount of acid to react, so the volume of CO_2 produced will be the same.

Sample GCSE questions

2   Hydrogen reacts with oxygen to make water. In this reaction, covalent bonds are broken and made, leading to an energy change.

$$2H_2(g) + O_2(g) \rightarrow 2H_2O(l)$$

Bond energies: H-H   436kJ/mol

                  O=O 498kJ/mol

                  H-O   464kJ/mol

(a)   **(i)**   Use the bond energy data to calculate the energy change for the reaction between hydrogen and oxygen.   **[3]**

bonds broken	bonds made
2×436	$\dfrac{4 \times 464}{}$
$+1 \times 498$	1856

Total   1370

$1370 - 1856 = -486\text{kJ/mol}$

Set out a 'balance sheet'.

Remember that you subtract the energy of the bonds made from the energy of the bonds broken to get the total energy change.

(ii)   Is the reaction exothermic or endothermic? Explain how you can tell.

Exothermic, because there is a negative value for total energy change.   **[2]**

(b)   **(i)**   A mixture of hydrogen gas with oxygen gas needs a spark to ignite it. Explain why a spark is needed at the start of the reaction.   **[2]**

The spark provides the activation energy, which is needed to break bonds at the start of the reaction.

(ii)   On the energy profile diagram, below, draw a line between the reactants and products that shows the need for a spark to ignite the mixture.   **[2]**

Activation energy for an exothermic reaction is shown as a 'hump', between the higher energy of the reactants and the energy of the products. For the second mark, the height of the hump should be marked and labelled, E_A or 'activation energy'.

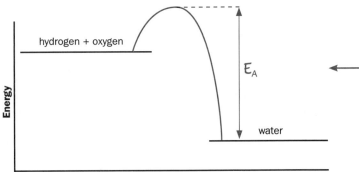

(iii)   Describe how the presence of a catalyst would alter the energy profile diagram.   **[1]**

The activation energy would be lower.

Exam practice questions

1 The relative atomic masses of calcium, carbon and oxygen are 40, 12 and 16, respectively.

(a) What is the relative formula mass of calcium carbonate, $CaCO_3$? [1]

....

(b) How many moles is 25 g of calcium carbonate? [1]

....

(c) What is the relative formula mass of calcium oxide, CaO? [1]

....

(d) What mass is lost when 100 g of calcium carbonate turns into calcium oxide? Explain this loss in mass. [2]

....

....

2 Magnesium metal burns in oxygen according to the equation:

$2Mg(s) + O_2(g) \rightarrow 2MgO(s)$

(a) What is the mass, in grams, of two moles of magnesium (relative atomic mass 24)? [1]

....

(b) What mass of oxygen (relative atomic mass 16) would this combine with? [1]

....

(c) What mass of magnesium oxide would be produced? [1]

....

(d) Calculate the mass of magnesium oxide produced by burning 6 g of magnesium. [2]

....

....

3 Look at the data table. It shows how temperature and pressure affect the yield (%) of the product in an industrial process.

Pressure (atmospheres)	Temperature (°C)			
	250	350	450	550
50	60%	30%	11%	4%
100	67%	34%	16%	7%
200	73%	50%	29%	14%

(a) What temperature gives the lowest yield? [1]

....

(b) What is the yield at 100 atmospheres pressure and a temperature of 350°C? [1]

....

Exam practice questions

(c) What happens to the yield as the temperature is decreased? **[1]**

....

4 (a) Explain what must happen to reactant particles for a reaction to take place. **[2]**

....

....

(b) Look at the graph below. The curve from the original reaction is labelled.

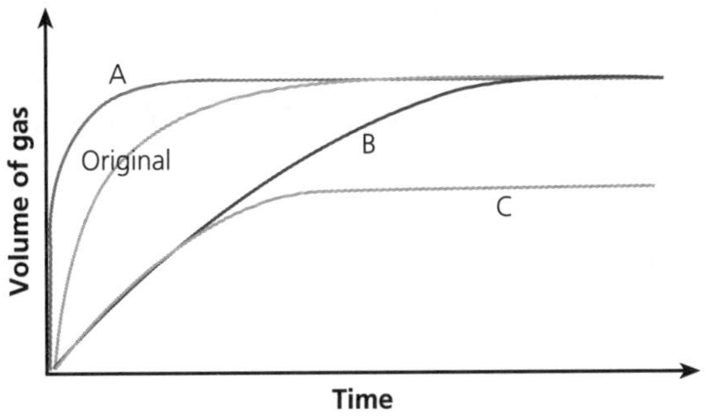

Select the curve on this graph that represents the curve showing the same reaction but using:

(i) a lower original temperature. **[1]**

....

(ii) half the original amount of reactants. **[1]**

....

(iii) Describe how you would use the graph to compare the speed of the original
reaction with the speed of reaction B. **[2]**

....

....

(c) Explain why some collisions do not result in a successful reaction. **[2]**

....

....

9 Forces and motion

The following topics are covered in this chapter:

- **Distance, speed and velocity**
- **Speed, velocity and acceleration**
- **Forces**
- **Acceleration and momentum**
- **Action and reaction**
- **Work and energy**
- **Energy and power**

9.1 Distance, speed and velocity

LEARNING SUMMARY

After studying this section, you should be able to:

- Explain the difference between average speed and instantaneous speed.
- Explain that velocity and displacement have direction.
- Calculate speeds, velocities, distances and times.
- Plot and interpret distance–time graphs.

Distance, speed and velocity

AQA	P2	✓
OCR A	P4	✓
OCR B	P3	✓
EDEXCEL	P2	✓
WJEC	P2	✓

Speed can be measured in metres per second (m/s) or kilometres per hour (km/h).

- An athlete running with a speed of 5 m/s travels a distance of 5 metres in one second and 10 metres in two seconds.
- An athlete with a faster speed of 8 m/s travels further, 8 metres, in each second and takes less time to complete his journey.

> **KEY POINT**
>
> To calculate speed:
>
> $$\text{speed (m/s)} = \frac{\text{distance (m)}}{\text{time (s)}}$$

Example of triangle method: $\text{speed} = \dfrac{\text{distance}}{\text{time}}$

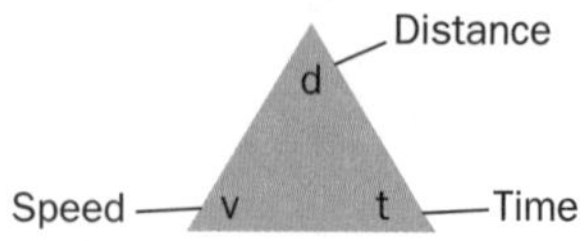

To calculate distance or time:

> Some students find using the triangle method useful to re-arrange a formula.

- Write the formula into a triangle, so that distance is 'over' time. This means putting distance at the top corner of the triangle.

- To find the **distance**, cover the word distance with your finger and look at the position of speed and time. They are side by side, so distance = speed × time.
- To find the **time**, cover the word time with your finger and distance is 'over' speed, so

$$\text{time} = \frac{\text{distance}}{\text{time}}$$

Speed and velocity

AQA	P2	✓
OCR A	P4	✓
OCR B	P3	✓
EDEXCEL	P2	✓
WJEC	P2	✓

Direction can be important when making calculations about a journey.

Speed does not take direction into account. Speed is calculated using the actual distance travelled no matter what direction the object is moving in. Speed is always a positive number.

If the direction travelled is taken into account, one direction can be called the positive direction and the opposite direction can be called the negative direction. The word displacement is used to measure distance with a direction. Travel in the positive direction is described as positive displacement and travel in the negative direction is described as negative displacement.

Quantities that have **magnitude** and **direction** are called **vectors**.

Velocity is speed in a given direction. Therefore, velocity is a vector. For example a dog walks in a positive direction for 5 m and then back again with a constant speed of 2 m/s, so he walks with a velocity of +2 m/s and then with a velocity of –2 m/s.

The total distance the dog has walked is 10 m, however the displacement at the end of the journey is zero.

$$\text{velocity (m/s)} = \frac{\text{displacement (m)}}{\text{time (s)}}$$

Distance-time graphs

AQA	P2	✓
OCR A	P4	✓
OCR B	P3	✓
EDEXCEL	P2	✓
WJEC	P2	✓

On a **distance-time graph**:

- A horizontal line means the object is stopped.
- A straight line sloping upwards means it has a steady speed.

Distance–time graph for a cycle ride.

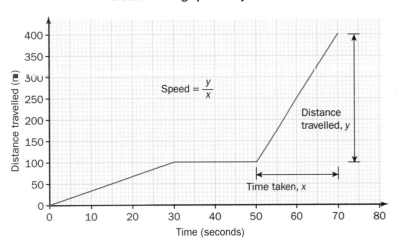

The steepness, or **gradient**, of the line shows the speed:

• A steeper gradient means a higher speed.
• A curved line means the speed is changing.

Example: Distance-time graph for a cycle ride.

Between 30 s and 50 s the cyclist stopped. The graph has a steeper gradient between 50 s and 70 s than between 0 s and 30 s. The cyclist was travelling at a greater speed.

To calculate a speed from a graph, work out the gradient of the straight line section

speed = $\frac{y}{x}$ where y = 400 m − 100 m = 300 m and x = 70 s − 50 s = 20 s.

speed = $\frac{400 \text{ m}}{20 \text{ s}}$ = 20 m/s.

Average speed and instantaneous speed

OCR A   P4   ✓

The **average speed** of the cyclist for the total journey shown on the graph on page 157 is:

= $\frac{\text{total distance}}{\text{total time}}$ = $\frac{400 \text{ m}}{70 \text{ s}}$ = 5.71 m/s

This is not the same as the **instantaneous speed** at any moment because the speed changes during the journey. If you calculate the average speed over a shorter time interval you get closer to the instantaneous speed.

Displacement–time graphs

OCR A   P4   ✓
OCR B   P3   ✓
EDEXCEL P2   ✓

If the direction of travel is being considered:

• A negative displacement is in the opposite direction to a positive displacement.
• A straight line sloping upwards or downwards means steady speed.
• Upwards means a steady positive velocity, and downwards means a steady negative velocity.

Example: Displacement–time graph for a journey from home.

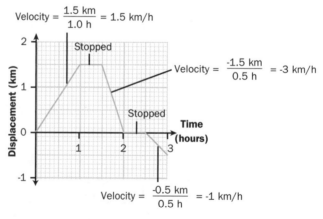

A boy starts from home (0 km) and walks to a shop, home again and then in the opposite direction to the shop.

1. What is the difference between instantaneous speed and average speed?
2. In the graph of the cycle ride, what is the speed during the first 30 seconds?
3. A car travels 288 km in three hours. Calculate the speed in km/h.
4. A car travels at a speed of 12 m/s. How long will it take to travel 1.44 km?
5. In the graph of the journey from home on page 158:
   a) What was the displacement after the first 30 minutes?
   b) When was the speed greatest?
   c) How can you tell this without doing any calculations?

1. Average speed is calculated from the distance travelled over time taken and the speed may have changed several times during the journey time. Instantaneous speed is the speed at any instant.
2. $(100 \text{ m} - 0 \text{ m}) \div (30 \text{ s} - 0 \text{ s}) = 3.33 \text{ m/s}$
3. $s = 288 \text{ km} \div 3 \text{ h} = 96 \text{ km/h}$
4. $t = d \div s \ t = 1.44 \text{ km} \div 12 \text{ m/s} = 1440 \text{ m} \div 12 \text{ m/s} = 120 \text{ s} \ (= 2 \text{ minutes})$
5. a) 0.75 km
   b) Between 1.5 and 2 hours (or on the way home from the shop).
   c) Because the graph is steepest at this point.

9.2 Speed, velocity and acceleration

LEARNING SUMMARY

After studying this section, you should be able to:

- Calculate acceleration.
- Plot and interpret speed–time graphs.
- Plot and interpret velocity–time graphs.
- Calculate acceleration and distance from graphs.

Acceleration

AQA	P2	✓
OCR A	P4	✓
OCR B	P3	✓
EDEXCEL	P2	✓
WJEC	P2	✓

Any change of velocity is called **acceleration**. Speeding up, slowing down and changing direction are all examples of acceleration. Acceleration is the change in velocity per second. It is measured in metres per second squared (m/s^2).

Example: If a car accelerates from 0 to 27 m/s (about 60 mph) in 6 seconds the change in velocity is 27 m/s, the acceleration

$$= \frac{27 \text{ m/s}}{6 \text{ s}} = 4.5 \text{ m/s}^2$$

> **KEY POINT**
>
> $$\text{acceleration (m/s}^2) = \frac{\text{change in velocity (m/s)}}{\text{time taken (s)}}$$
>
> $$a = \frac{(v - u)}{t}$$
>
> where a is the acceleration of an object whose velocity changes from initial velocity (u) to final velocity (v) in time (t).

Example: A car accelerates from 14 m/s to 30 m/s in 8 s. The acceleration:

$$a = \frac{(30 \text{ m/s} - 14 \text{ m/s})}{6 \text{ s}} = \frac{16 \text{ m/s}}{8 \text{ s}} = 2 \text{ m/s}^2$$

Speed–time graphs

AQA	P2	✓
OCR A	P4	✓
OCR B	P3	✓
EDEXCEL	P2	✓
WJEC	P2	✓

Plotting the speed of an object against the time gives a graph like this:

A speed–time graph.

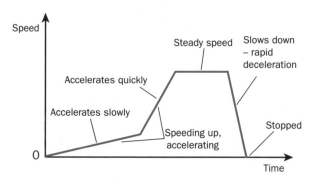

> Always check carefully whether a graph is a speed–time graph or a distance–time graph.

- A **positive slope (gradient)** means that the speed is increasing - the object is accelerating.
- A **horizontal line** means that the object is travelling at a steady speed.
- A **negative slope (gradient)** means the speed is decreasing – negative acceleration.
- A **curved slope** means that the acceleration is changing – the object has **non-uniform acceleration**.

On true **speed–time graphs** the speed has only positive values. On **velocity–time graphs** the velocity can be negative.

> For OCR B you need to know about speed cameras.

Tachographs are instruments that are put in lorry cabs to check that the lorry has not exceeded the speed limit and that the driver has stopped for breaks. They draw a graph of the speed against time for the lorry.

Velocity–time graphs

AQA	P2	✓
OCR A	P4	✓
OCR B	P3	✓
EDEXCEL	P2	✓
WJEC	P2	✓

Graphs for a ball that rolls up a hill, slows and rolls back down, speeding up.

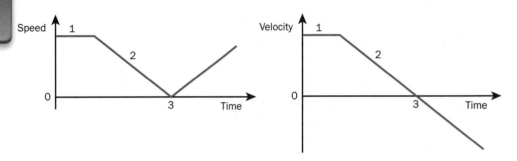

At point 3 the ball stops and starts to roll back. Its speed starts to increase again. Its velocity starts to increase, but it is now rolling downhill – so the velocity is negative.

Acceleration from a graph

The acceleration is the gradient of a velocity–time graph.

Example: A graph of velocity against time for a car journey.

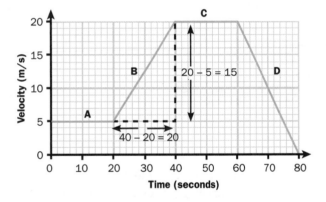

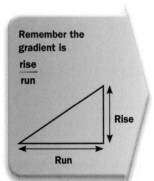

Remember the gradient is

$$\frac{\text{rise}}{\text{run}}$$

In part B of the graph the car accelerates from 5 m/s to 20 m/s in (40 − 20)s = 20 seconds. The gradient:

$$= \frac{y}{x} = \frac{15}{20} = 0.75$$

So the acceleration = 0.75 m/s².

Distance travelled from a graph

AQA	P2	✓
OCR B	P3	✓
EDEXCEL	P2	✓
WJEC	P2	✓

On a velocity–time graph the area between the graph and the time axis represents the distance travelled.

Example: Distance travelled on a bike journey.

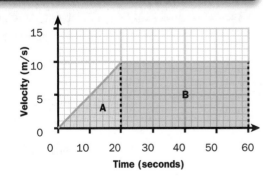

Take care with units. You may need to change minutes or hours to seconds, or kilometres to metres.

36 km/h =

$\dfrac{36 \times 1000}{60 \times 60}$ m/s

= 10 m/s

Also remember to write down the units for your answer.

The distance travelled = area under A + area under B

Area A = area of pink triangle = $\dfrac{1}{2}$ (10 m/s × 20 s) = 100 m

Area B = area of blue rectangle = 10 m/s × (60 – 20) s = 400 m

Distance travelled = 100 m + 400 m = 500 m

PROGRESS CHECK

1. A car accelerates from 0 to 24 m/s in 8 s. What is the acceleration?
2. What does a horizontal line on a speed-time graph tell you?
3. From graph of the car journey on page 161, what is the acceleration at:
   a) A
   b) D.
4. Sketch a velocity time graph for a car that speeds up in a negative direction, travels at a steady speed, and then slows down and stops.
5. From graph of the car journey on page 161, what is the distance travelled in section:
   a) C
   b) D.

5. C 20m/s × (60 s – 40 s) = 400 m
   D $\frac{1}{2}$ × 20 m/s × (80 s – 60 s) = 200 m
4. Line goes below x axis similar to last part of the graph for the rolling ball, then horizontal, then straight line sloping upwards to the x axis again.
3. A 0 m/s^2
   D (0 – 20) m/s ÷ (80 – 60) s = – 1 m/s^2
2. The object is travelling at a steady/constant speed.
1. 24 m/s ÷ 8s = 3 m/s^2

9.3 Forces

LEARNING SUMMARY

After studying this section, you should be able to:

- Explain the difference between mass and weight.
- Calculate the resultant force on an object.
- Describe the forces on moving and stationary objects.
- Understand and use Newton's First Law of Motion.

Mass and weight

AQA	P2	✓
OCR A	P4	✓
OCR B	P3	✓
EDEXCEL	P2	✓
WJEC	P2	✓

For WJEC you also need to know that mass gives an object inertia.

KEY POINT

Mass is measured in **kilograms** (kg). It is the amount of matter in an object. An object has the same mass everywhere, on the Earth, the Moon, or in outer space.

Weight is a force and is measured in **newtons** (N). Weight is the force of gravity attracting the mass towards the centre of the Earth. An object's weight changes when the force of gravity changes, for example, on the Earth, the Moon, or in outer space.

weight (N) = mass (kg) × gravitational field strength (N/kg)

Gravitational field strength close to the surface of the Earth is 10 N/kg. Objects in free fall have a constant acceleration of 10 m/s^2.

In outer space there is no gravity so all objects are weightless. The Moon's gravitational attraction is only one sixth of the Earth's, so objects on the Moon have only one sixth their weight on Earth.

> For OCR B you need to know that g will be slightly less on top of a mountain and more at the bottom of a mine shaft.

To remember the differences between mass and weight think of a tin of beans.

- It is weightless in outer space.
- It has less weight on the Moon.
- Its mass changes if you eat the beans.

Resultant and balanced forces

AQA	P2	✓
OCR A	P4	✓
OCR B	P3	✓
EDEXCEL	P2	✓
WJEC	P2	✓

Forces have size and direction. On diagrams they are shown by arrows. The length of the arrow represents the size of the force. When several forces act on an object the effect is the same as one force in a certain direction. This is called the **resultant force**. Forces combine to give a resultant force. If the resultant force is zero the forces on the object are **balanced**.

Resultant forces.

Forces on an object:

2 N
1 N

0.5 N ↑↓ 1 N
1.5 N

2 N
1 N

Equivalent resultant force:

3 N

resultant = 0

1 N

KEY POINT

A resultant force changes the velocity of an object. This idea is known as **Newtons First Law of Motion**:

If the resultant force on an object is zero, the object will remain stationary or continue to move at a steady speed in the same direction.

When forces on an object are balanced it does not fall.

Reaction and tension are forces that can balance weight.

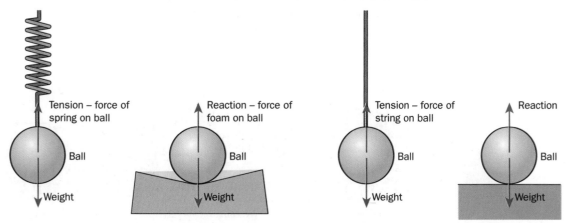

Tension – force of spring on ball · Ball · Weight

Reaction – force of foam on ball · Ball · Weight

Tension – force of string on ball · Ball · Weight

Reaction · Ball · Weight

The upward force of the spring, or the foam, trying to return to their original shape, balances the weight.

Even though the changes in shape are too small for us to see, the restoring force – the tension in the string or the reaction from the floor – balances the weight.

Forces and elasticity

AQA   P2   ✓

A force acting on an object may change the shape of the object, for example in the case of the spring or the foam on page 163. Objects like these are elastic, and as the object stretches it stores **elastic potential energy**. When a spring is stretched the work done on it is equal to the energy stored. This energy is released when the spring returns to its original length.

> **KEY POINT**
>
> The extension of a spring is proportional to the force applied, provided the limit of proportionality is not exceeded.
>
> $F = k \times e$
>
> where F is the force in newtons (N), e is the extension in metres (m) and k is the spring constant in newtons per metre (N/m)

Stretching a spring, P, is the limit of proportionality.

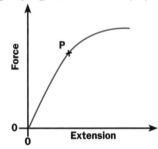

Friction

AQA   P2   ✓
OCR A   P4   ✓
OCR B   P3   ✓
EDEXCEL   P2   ✓
WJEC   P2   ✓

When one object slides, or tries to slide, over another, there is **friction**. Friction is the resistive force between the two surfaces.

Air resistance is the resistive force that acts against objects moving through the air.

Drag is the resistive force on objects moving through liquids or gases. Drag is larger in liquids.

Drag can be reduced by shaping the object so that it is more streamlined.

These resistive forces:

- Always act against the direction of motion.
- Are zero when there is no movement.
- Increase as the speed of the object increases.

The forces on a cyclist when speeding up, at a constant speed and slowing down.

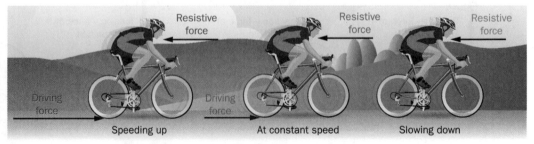

Speeding up   At constant speed   Slowing down

> Friction can be reduced by lubricants.

When the driving force is larger than the resistive force the cyclist speeds up, when they are equal he travels at a steady speed and when the resistive force is greater he slows down.

Forces when falling

AQA	P2	✓
OCR A	P4	✓
OCR B	P3	✓
EDEXCEL	P2	✓
WJEC	P2	✓

The resultant force on a skydiver changes.

Falling objects reach a steady speed called the **terminal velocity,** when:

air resistance = weight

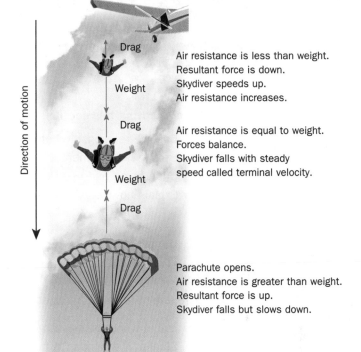

Forces when skydiving.

Air resistance is less than weight.
Resultant force is down.
Skydiver speeds up.
Air resistance increases.

Air resistance is equal to weight.
Forces balance.
Skydiver falls with steady speed called terminal velocity.

Parachute opens.
Air resistance is greater than weight.
Resultant force is up.
Skydiver falls but slows down.

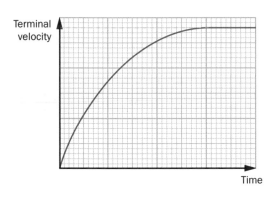

A falling object eventually reaches a terminal velocity.

In a vacuum, there is no air resistance so objects continue to fall with acceleration and acceleration due to gravity at 10 m/s.

> It's a common mistake to think that there is always a force in the direction of movement.

If an object is travelling at a steady speed there is no resultant force on it. When an object is slowing down the resultant force on it is opposite to its direction.

PROGRESS CHECK

1. What is the weight of 2 kg of sugar?
2. The driving force is 3000 N and friction is 900 N. What is the resultant force?
3. A car with steady speed of 100 km/h travels in a straight line. What is the resultant force?
4. Draw the forces on a book placed on a table.
5. How much does a 100 g apple weigh **a)** on Earth and **b)** on the Moon?
6. The driving force is 2500 N, friction is 800 N and air resistance is 1700 N.
   a) What is the resultant force?
   b) What happens to the car?

9.4 Acceleration and momentum

LEARNING SUMMARY

After studying this section, you should be able to:

- Use the relationship between force, mass and acceleration.
- Explain how momentum is calculated.
- Understand and use Newton's Second Law of Motion.
- Explain how collisions can be made safer.

Force, acceleration and momentum

AQA	P2	✓
OCR A	P4	✓
OCR B	P3	✓
EDEXCEL	P2	✓
WJEC	P2	✓

A resultant force on an object causes it to accelerate. The acceleration is:

- Larger if the force is larger.
- Smaller if the mass is larger.
- In the same direction as the force.

KEY POINT

For a resultant force on an object:

force (N) = mass (kg) × acceleration (m/s^2)

$F = ma$

where F = force, m = mass and a = acceleration.

The **momentum** of an object is:

- Larger for a larger velocity.
- Larger for a larger mass.
- In the same direction as the velocity.
- Measured in units called kg m/s or Ns (they are the same).

momentum (kg m/s or Ns) = mass (kg) × velocity (m/s)

momentum = mv where v = velocity

Momentum = mv Momentum = $-MV$

> To remember what momentum depends on, think about 10 pin bowling. You are more likely to knock pins down with more momentum. This could be a ball with a lot of mass or a ball with a high velocity.

When a resultant force acts on an object, it causes a change in momentum in the same direction as the force (because the velocity changes). The bigger the force and the longer the time that the force acts, the bigger the change in momentum:

change in momentum (kg m/s or Ns) = force (N) × time (s)

Newton's second law of motion

AQA	P2	✓
OCR A	P4	✓
OCR B	P3	✓
EDEXCEL	P2	✓
WJEC	P2	✓

KEY POINT

Newton's Second Law of Motion states:

When a resultant force acts on an object, it causes a change in momentum in the same direction as the force. The resultant force equals the rate of change of momentum.

$$\text{force (N)} = \frac{\text{change in momentum (kg m/s or Ns)}}{\text{time (s)}}$$

$$F = \frac{(mv - mu)}{t}$$

where t = time, u = initial velocity and v = final velocity.

The equation $F = ma$ is another way of saying this because acceleration

> You do not need to be able to show or explain this.

$$a = \frac{(v - u)}{t}$$

$$F = \frac{m(v - u)}{t} = \frac{(mv - mu)}{t}$$

Safer collisions

AQA	P2	✓
OCR A	P4	✓
OCR B	P3	✓
EDEXCEL	P2	✓
WJEC	P2	✓

In a collision, a force brings your body to a sudden stop. The larger the stopping force on the body the more it is damaged. To reduce damage we must reduce the force:

change of momentum = force × time

For the same change in momentum, to reduce the force we must increase the time to stop. If the collision takes place over a longer time, say 0.5 s instead of 0.05 s – ten times as long – then the stopping force will only be one tenth of the size. The time of a collision can be increased by using:

● **Crumple zones** in the car. The front and back of the car are designed to crumple in a collision, increasing the distance and time over which the occupants are brought to a stop.

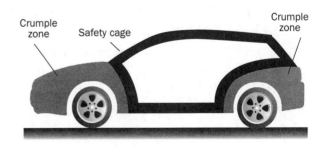

Crumple zone | Safety cage | Crumple zone

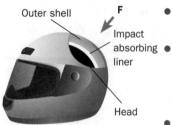

Outer shell

F

Impact absorbing liner

Head

Do not confuse momentum with energy. Momentum has a direction and is measured in Ns or kg m/s. Energy, like mass, has no direction and it is measured in Joules (J). 1 J = 1 Nm – a different unit.

- The body hits the **airbag**, which is compressed, increasing the distance the body moves and the time it takes to stop.
- **Seatbelts** are designed to stretch slightly so that the body moves forward and comes to a stop more slowly with a smaller deceleration than it would if it hit the windscreen or front seats. After a collision the seatbelts should be replaced because having stretched once they may not work properly again.
- **Cycle and motor-cycle helmets** contain a layer of material which will compress on impact so that the skull is brought to a stop more slowly. They should be replaced after a collision as the material will be damaged and may not protect effectively again.

Other examples of reducing the force by increasing the time taken to stop include:

- Crash barriers that crumple on impact.
- Bending knees when landing after jumping.
- Bubble wrap.
- Sprung floors in gyms.

Objects that change shape absorb energy and sometimes heat up noticeably.

PROGRESS CHECK

1. Calculate the resultant force on a 1200 kg car accelerating at 3 m/s^2.
2. Calculate the momentum of a ball of mass 2 kg and velocity 5 m/s.
3. Calculate the momentum of a ball of mass 200 g and velocity 8 m/s travelling in the opposite direction.
4. A force of 50 N acts on a stationary object for 12 seconds. Calculate its gain in momentum.
5. A runaway truck of mass 1000 kg and velocity 12 m/s came to a sudden stop in 0.002 s.
   a) Calculate the stopping force on the truck.
   b) A crash barrier would have allowed the truck to stop over the greater time of 0.5 s. What would the stopping force have been?
   c) What difference would this make?

c) There would be less damage to the truck.
b) force = (1000 kg × 12 m/s) ÷ 0.5 s = 24 000 N
5. a) force = (1000 kg × 12 m/s) ÷ 0.002 s = 6 000 000 N
4. 50 N × 12s = 600 Ns
3. 0.2 kg × (−8 m/s) = − 1.6 kgm/s (or −1.6 Ns)
2. 2 kg × 5 m/s = 10 kgm/s (or 10 Ns)
1. 1200 kg × 3 m/s^2 = 3600 N

9.5 Action and reaction

LEARNING SUMMARY

After studying this section, you should be able to:

- Explain that forces always occur in pairs.
- Identify an interaction of pair of forces.
- Use Newton's Third Law of Motion to calculate forces.
- Use conservation of momentum to calculate velocities.

Interaction pairs

AQA	P2	✓
OCR A	P4	✓
EDEXCEL	P2	✓
WJEC	P2	✓

When two objects interact there is always an **interaction pair of forces**. As these skaters show, the man in red cannot push the man in blue without the man in blue pushing the man in red.

When two skaters push each other, they both move backwards.

Push

In an interaction pair of forces, the two forces:

- Are always equal in size and opposite in direction.
- Always act on different objects.
- Are always the same type of force (for example, contact forces, gravitational forces, or magnetic forces).

> **KEY POINT**
>
> This idea is known as **Newton's Third Law of Motion** which states:
>
> *When two objects interact, the forces they exert on each other are equal and opposite and are called action and reaction forces.*

Friction and getting started

| OCR A | P4 | ✓ |

Friction is the reaction force needed for walking or wheeled transport.

Forces that make a wheel move forward.

Action Force   **Reaction Force**

To remember how friction gets you moving, think of trying to cycle or walk on a frictionless icy surface. There is no reaction force. You would slip backwards and never move forward.

- **Action force** is where the wheel pushes back on the road.
- **Reaction force** is where the road pushes forward on the wheel, which sends the wheel forward.

When you walk your foot pushes back on the ground and the ground pushes your foot forward.

Weight and the Earth

| OCR A | P4 | ✓ |
| OCR B | P3 | ✓ |

The weight of an object is the gravitational attraction towards the centre of the Earth. The other force of this interaction pair acts on the Earth. It is the gravitational attraction of the object attracting the whole Earth. We do not notice this effect because the mass of the Earth is so large.

Do not confuse interaction pairs of forces, which act on different objects, with balanced forces, which act on the same object.

An action and reaction pair of forces.

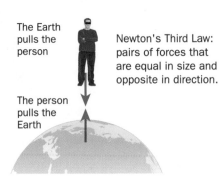

The Earth pulls the person

Newton's Third Law: pairs of forces that are equal in size and opposite in direction.

The person pulls the Earth

The reaction force from a surface *balances* the weight of the object. It is not the reaction pair of the weight, because:

- It is a different type of force (a contact force, not gravitational).
- It acts on the same object.

Rockets and jet engines

| OCR A | P4 | ✓ |

Rockets and jet engines both produce hot exhaust gases. These are pushed out of the back of the engines. There is an equal and opposite reaction force that sends the rocket or jet forward.

Conservation of momentum and rocket propulsion.

For OCR B you need to be able to apply particle theory to rocket exhaust gases.

Exhaust gases gain momentum in this direction

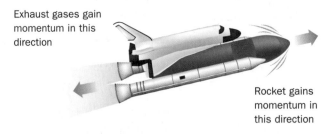

Rocket gains momentum in this direction

Conservation of momentum

AQA	P2	✓
OCR A	P4	✓
EDEXCEL	P2	✓

When two objects **collide** or **explode apart** there is an equal and opposite force on each object, and they interact (push against each other) for the same time. This means that the change in the momentum of the objects is equal and opposite. Another way to say this is that **momentum is conserved**.

The total momentum of the two objects before the collision or explosion is the same as the total momentum after.

Example: When two objects collide and stick together.

Two objects colliding and sticking together.

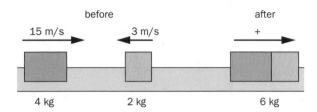

Before the collision momentum:

= 4 kg × 15 m/s + 2 kg × (–3) m/s = (60 – 6) kg m/s

After the collision:

momentum = 6 kg × v

So, because of conservation of momentum

v = 9 m/s

Recoil

OCR A   P4   ✓

When a bullet leaves a gun, action and reaction, or **conservation of momentum**, tell us the gun must recoil.

Example: A 0.8 g paintball is fired at 80 m/s from a 3 kg paintball marker.

Firing a paintball.

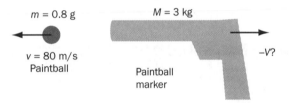

Conservation of momentum: $m\ v = M\ V$

Recoil velocity:

$$V = \frac{0.8\ g \times 80\ m/s}{3000\ g} = 0.02\ m/s$$

PROGRESS CHECK

1. A girl pushes on a wall with a force of 5 N. Describe the reaction force.
2. Why is it difficult to walk on ice?
3. How does a rocket move in outer space where there is nothing to push against to get moving?
4. When you release a partly inflated balloon it flies around as it deflates. Explain why.
5. A book is placed on a table. What are the two interaction pairs of forces?
6. A toy car with mass 0.5 kg and speed 4 m/s collides with a toy truck of mass 2 kg. They both stop. What was the speed of the truck?

PROGRESS CHECK

1. The wall pushes on the girl with a force of 5 N.
2. Because there is little friction to push back on your foot and send you forward.
3. It pushes exhaust gases out the back, so there is an equal and opposite force pushing the rocket forward.
4. The balloon pushes air out of the back and an equal and opposite force on the balloon pushes it forward.
5. The weight of the book and the equal and opposite gravitational attraction of the book on the Earth.
   The contact force of the book pushing down on the table, and the equal and opposite force of the table pushing up on the book.
6. They both stop (momentum = 0), so before the collision the momentum of the car is equal and opposite to the momentum of the truck.
   Car: $mv = 0.5$ kg × 4 m/s = 2 kgm/s Truck: $MV = 2$ kg × V $V = -2$ kgm/s ÷ 2 kg = −1 m/s

9.6 Work and energy

LEARNING SUMMARY

After studying this section, you should be able to:

- Relate energy transfers to work done.
- Calculate changes in gravitational potential energy.
- Calculate the kinetic energy of moving objects.
- Recognise when the change in GPE = the change in KE and use this in calculations.

Work and energy

AQA	P2	✓
OCR A	P4	✓
OCR B	P3	✓
EDEXCEL	P2	✓
WJEC	P2	✓

When a **force** makes something move, **work** is done. The amount of work done is equal to the amount of energy transferred. Work and energy are measured in joules (J):

KEY POINT

work done by a force (J) = force (N) × distance moved by force in direction of the force (m)

When work is done *by* something it loses energy, when work is done *on* something it gains energy.

Gravitational potential energy

AQA	P2	✓
OCR A	P4	✓
OCR B	P3	✓
EDEXCEL	P2	✓
WJEC	P2	✓

A rollercoaster at the top of a slope has stored energy, which is called **gravitational potential energy (GPE)**, or sometimes **potential energy (PE)**. This is the stored energy that an object has because of its position, in this case, higher above the surface of the Earth.

Example: Doing work – increasing the GPE.

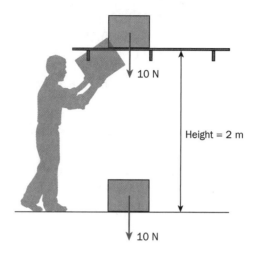

Doing work – increasing the GPE.

10 N

Height = 2 m

10 N

> It's the change in GPE that depends on the change in height.

When you lift a 10 N weight (a mass of 1 kg) from the floor to a high shelf, a height difference of 2 m, you have done work on the weight.

The work done = 10 N × 2 m = 20 J and this is equal to the increase in the GPE of the weight.

> **KEY POINT**
>
> **Change in GPE (J) = weight (N) × vertical height difference (m)**

> **KEY POINT**
>
> **Change in GPE = _m g h_;** where _g_ = the gravitational field strength (N/kg) _m_ = mass (kg) and _h_ = height change (m).

Example: To calculate a change in height from change in GPE.

A mass of 2 kg is lifted up and gains 400 J of GPE (gravitational field strength, _g_ = 10N/kg).

Change in height _h_:

$$= \frac{400 \text{ J}}{2 \text{ kg} \times 10 \text{ N/kg}} = 20 \text{ m}$$

Work and energy

AQA	P2	✓
OCR A	P4	✓
OCR B	P3	✓
EDEXCEL	P2	✓
WJEC	P2	✓

An object that is moving has **kinetic energy (KE)**. The energy depends on the mass of the object and on the square of the speed. Doubling the speed gives four times the energy.

Example: An air hockey puck, floating on an air table, is almost frictionless. A force does work on the puck – it pushes it a small distance. Energy is transferred and the kinetic energy of the puck increases – it speeds up. When the force stops the puck moves at a constant speed across the table – its kinetic energy is now constant.

AQA   P2   ✓
OCR A   P4   ✓
OCR B   P3   ✓
EDEXCEL P2   ✓
WJEC   P2   ✓

KEY POINT

kinetic energy (J) = $\frac{1}{2}$ × mass (kg) × [speed (m/s)]^2

Energy does not have a direction. Speed or velocity can be used to calculate the kinetic energy.

KE = $\frac{1}{2}$ m v^2 where m = mass (kg) v = speed (m/s).

Example: To calculate the speed of an object from its KE.

A mass of 2 kg has 400 J of KE.

speed $v = \sqrt{\dfrac{(2 \times 400J)}{2\ kg}}$ = 20 m/s

Calculations with GPE and KE

When frictional forces are small enough to be ignored the transfer of energy between KE and GPE can be used to calculate heights and speeds.

Example: A car is driven by a trackside motor to the top of a rollercoaster and then freewheels down the slope. Assume that the GPE at the bottom of the slope is zero.

Transferring energy from GPE to KE and back again.

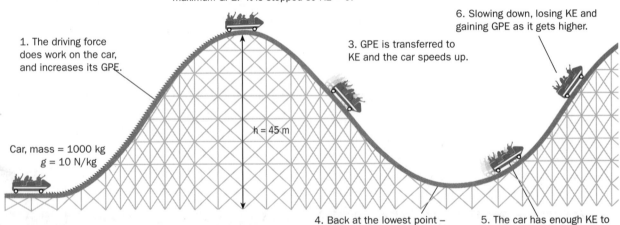

2. The highest point – the car has maximum GPE. It is stopped so KE = 0.

6. Slowing down, losing KE and gaining GPE as it gets higher.

1. The driving force does work on the car, and increases its GPE.

3. GPE is transferred to KE and the car speeds up.

h = 45 m

Car, mass = 1000 kg
g = 10 N/kg

4. Back at the lowest point – maximum KE and GPE = 0.

5. The car has enough KE to continue up the next slope.

Increase in GPE of car:

= $m\ g\ h$ = 1000 kg × 10 N/kg × 45 m = 450 000 J

Assuming there are no friction forces as the car travels down the slope:

Loss of GPE = gain in KE

gain in KE = 450 000J

450 000 J = $\frac{1}{2}$ m v^2 = $\frac{1}{2}$ × 1000 kg × v^2

v^2 = 900 (m/s)^2 so speed v = 30 m/s

Remember to square a number by multiplying it by itself. A calculator is useful for finding the square root of a number.

1. What is the work done by a tractor that pulls a trailer with a force of 1000 N across a 200 m field?
2. A rollercoaster car that has a weight of 12 000 N goes to the top of a 30 m slope. What is the gain in GPE?
3. A 900 kg car is travelling at 15 m/s. What is its KE?
4. A toy car rolls down a slope. The gain in KE is less than the loss in PE. Suggest why.
5. A lift weighs 8000 N it is raised a height of 50 m.
   a) What is the gain in GPE?
   b) What is the work done on the lift by the motor?

1. 1000 N × 200 m = 200 000 J
2. 12 000 N × 30 m = 360 000 J
3. ½ × 900 kg × (15 m/s)² = 101 250 J
4. If there is friction some of the energy is not transferred from GPE to KE, i.e. it is transferred to heat energy.
5 a) 8000 N × 50 m = 400 000 J
  b) 400 000 J

9.7 Energy and power

LEARNING SUMMARY

After studying this section, you should be able to:

- Explain and use the principle of conservation of energy.
- Explain what happens to the GPE of an object falling with terminal velocity.
- Calculate shopping distances.
- Describe factors that affect stopping distances.
- Use the relationship between power, energy transferred and home.

Conservation of energy

OCR A	P4	✓
EDEXCEL	P2	✓
WJEC	P2	✓

The **principle of conservation of energy** says that the total energy always remains the same. When energy is transferred to the surroundings by heating due to frictional forces it is no longer useful, but it is not lost. We say it has been **dissipated** (spread out) as heat.

The relationship 'gain in KE = loss in GPE' is only true for a falling object if the air resistance (or drag) is small and can be ignored, or if the object is falling in a vacuum.

Work against friction

AQA	P2	✓
OCR A	P4	✓
OCR B	P3	✓
WJEC	P2	✓

A skydiver eventually reaches **terminal velocity**. She is still falling, so GPE is being lost, but no KE is being gained. The energy is being used to do work against the frictional force (air resistance.) The skydiver and surrounding air will heat up.

Forces when skydiving.

Air resistance

Weight

The space shuttle, with a lot of KE, needed heat proof tiles to protect it from the heat resulting from doing work against air resistance when it re-entered the Earth's atmosphere.

When a cyclist pedals, but travels at a steady speed, work is done against air resistance and friction. Energy is transferred and heats the bicycle and surroundings. No energy is being transferred as KE to the bicycle unless it speeds up.

Stopping distances

AQA	P2	✓
OCR B	P3	✓
EDEXCEL	P2	✓
WJEC	P2	✓

The distance travelled between the driver noticing a hazard and the vehicle being stationary is called the **stopping distance**.

KEY POINT

- Stopping distance = thinking distance + braking distance.
- **Thinking distance** is distance travelled during the driver's reaction time – the time between seeing the hazard and applying the brakes.
- **Braking distance** is the distance travelled while the vehicle is braking.

This diagram shows the shortest stopping distances at different speeds

The stopping distance increases with speed.

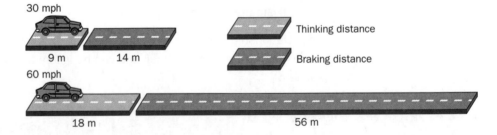

30 mph

9 m   14 m   Thinking distance

    Braking distance

60 mph

18 m   56 m

When speed doubles:

- Thinking distance doubles.
- Braking distance is four times as far.

The stopping distances are also longer if:

- The driver is tired, affected by some drugs (including alcohol and some medicines) or distracted and not concentrating, so thinking distance is increased.
- The road is wet or icy or the tyres or brakes are in poor condition. The friction forces will be less so the braking distance is increased.
- The vehicle is fully loaded with passengers or goods. The extra mass reduces the deceleration during braking, so the braking distance is increased.

These stopping distances are taken into account when setting road speed limits. Drivers should not drive closer than the thinking distance to the car in front, to allow for time to react. They should reduce speed in bad weather to allow for the increased braking distance.

Braking and kinetic energy

AQA	P2	✓
OCR B	P3	✓
EDEXCEL	P2	✓
WJEC	P2	✓

- When speed doubles reaction time is the same:

  thinking distance = speed × reaction time (thinking distance doubles)

- Work done by the brakes against friction = loss in KE

  braking force × braking distance = $\frac{1}{2}mv^2$

  $$\text{braking distance} = \frac{\text{mass} \times \text{speed}^2}{2 \times \text{braking force}}$$

  The braking distance is four times as far.

> For OCR B you need to be able to draw and interpret graphs of stopping distance and about ABS brakes.

KEY POINT

The **thinking distance** depends on **speed**.

The **braking distance** depends on **(speed)^2**.

Example: At three times the speed, braking distance is nine times as far.

Power

AQA	P2	✓
OCR B	P3	✓
EDEXCEL	P2	✓

KEY POINT

Power is the work done, or energy transferred, divided by time. Power is measured in watts (W).

$$\text{power (W)} = \frac{\text{work done or energy transferred (J)}}{\text{time (s)}}$$

Power is also the rate of energy transfer.

> Units can help you to remember how things are related and do calculations. A watt is a joule per second, so divide energy (joules) by time (seconds) to get power (watts).

Example: A 7.5 kW crane lifts a 3000 N weight up a height of 10 m. How long does it take?

$$7.5 \text{ kW} = \frac{3000 \text{ N} \times 10 \text{ m}}{t}$$

$$t = \frac{30\,000 \text{ J}}{7500 \text{ W}} = 4 \text{ s}$$

Don't forget to use the correct units in your calculations. It can help to change everything to the basic units, for example kilowatts to watts. An answer without units is not an answer – it's just a number.

PROGRESS CHECK

1. Under what conditions is the 'loss in GPE = gain in KE' ?
2. What happens to the GPE when an object falls with terminal velocity?
3. Give an example where stopping distances would be longer than shown in the diagram.
4. A worker does 1000 J of work in 5 s. What power was used?
5. What happens to the energy transferred by a pedalling cyclist when travelling at a steady speed?
6. Calculate the stopping distance of the car in the diagram when travelling at 90 mph.

1. When the frictional forces are so small they can be ignored, or in a vacuum.
2. The GPE is transferred to heating the air and the object.
3. Any of listed examples e.g. driver has been drinking or poor condition of tyres.
4. 1000 J ÷ 5 s = 200 W
5. The cyclist is doing work against friction forces the energy is transferred as heat to the bicycle, road and air.
6. 3 × 30mph so thinking distance = 3 × 9 m braking distance = 9 × 14 m stopping distance = 153 m

Sample GCSE questions

1 An aircraft with a mass of 9000 kg is flying at a level height above the ground.

Lift 90 kN

Thrust 100 kN ⟵

⟶ Drag 5 kN

Weight (gravity) 90 kN

(a) Calculate the acceleration of the aircraft. **[4]**

$force = 100\ kN - 5\ kN = 95\ kN$ ⟵ Work out the resultant force forwards

$F = ma$ ⟵ Show which equation you are using

$95\ kN = 9000\ kg \times a$

$a = \dfrac{95\ kN}{9000\ kg}$ ⟵ Write down the calculation – if you do it incorrectly you may still get a mark.

$a = 10.6\ m/s^2$ ⟵ Remember the units

(b) Draw a ring around the two quantities of the aircraft that are increasing. **[2]**

acceleration

gravitational potential energy

height

kinetic energy

momentum

(c) After some time, the aircraft stops accelerating and travels at a steady speed although the driving force is still 100 kN. Describe how the speed of the aircraft changes during its level flight and explain why this happens. *The quality of your written communication will be assessed in this answer.* **[6]**

As the aircraft accelerates it gets faster and the drag force on it increases. This is because the drag force increases with speed. As the drag force increases the resultant force forwards is reduced. This means that the acceleration is reduced. So as the ⟵ aircraft gets faster its acceleration gets lower until eventually, at the top speed, the acceleration is zero and the aircraft no longer accelerates. This speed is called the terminal velocity.

Marks will be awarded depending on the number of relevant points included in the answer and the spelling, punctuation and grammar. In this question there are 6 or 7 relevant points so 5 or 6 points with good spelling punctuation and grammar will gain full marks.

[Total = 12]

Sample GCSE questions

2 This graph shows the velocity of a car for part of its journey.

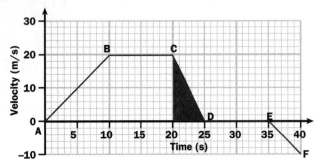

(a) Describe the motion of the car during the journey. *The quality of your written communication will be assessed in this answer.* **[6]**

At point A the car is stationary. It accelerates with constant acceleration for 10 seconds to a speed of 20 m/s at point B. From B to C it travels at a steady speed of 20 m/s. From C to D it slows down to a stop over 5 seconds. From D to E it is stationary for 10 seconds and from E to F it accelerates in the opposite direction for 5 seconds, reaching a speed of 10 m/s back towards the start.

(b) What is the acceleration of the car between A and B?

$$acceleration = \frac{change\ in\ speed}{time}$$

Change in speed = (20 m/s – 0 m/s) time = 10 s
Acceleration = 20 m/s ÷ 10 s = 2 m/s^2

Acceleration = ...2.......m/s^2 **[2]**

> State the equation you use.
>
> The acceleration is the gradient of the line, so, instead of using the equation, you could have explained that you were working out the gradient.

(c) What is the distance travelled between points C and D?

distance = shaded area under the line
Area of triangle made by CD = $\frac{1}{2}$ x (20 m/s x 5 s) = 50 m

Distance travelled = ...50.......m **[2]**

> Show what you are calculating, you may still get a mark if you later make a mistake.

(d) The distance travelled between the point A and point C is 300 m.

(i) Calculate the average velocity between point A and point C.

$$v = \frac{total\ distance}{time} \qquad v = \frac{300\ m}{20\ s} = 15\ m/s$$

(ii) Compare your value for the average velocity with the velocity at point C on the graph, and explain why they are different. **[3]**

The velocity at point C on the graph is 20 m/s which is greater than the average velocity between A and C of 15 m/s. This is because 20 m/s is the instantaneous velocity and not the average velocity. The average velocity is reduced by the fact that between A and B the velocity was less than 20 m/s.

[Total = 13]

Exam practice questions

1 These statements describe what happens during a parachute jump.

A	The parachute opens – increasing the drag force
(B)	His speed increases and the drag force increases
C	The drag force becomes equal to his weight
(D)	The skydiver steps from the aircraft and falls, he accelerates at 10 m/s^2
E	He falls with a constant speed
F	His speed decreases

Put them in the correct order, the first one has been done for you.   **[4]**

D					

2 In a test a 1200 kg car crashes into the back of a 3000 kg lorry:

v = 15m/s

v = 20m/s

M = 1200kg   *M* = 3000kg

The car has velocity 20 m/s.

(a) Calculate the momentum of the car before the collision.   **[2]**

....

(b) In a collision the total momentum of the car and the lorry   **[1]**

 A is increased

 B is reduced

 C stays the same

 D may do any of the above.

 ☐

(c) The momentum of the lorry is 45 000 kgm/s.
 The car and truck stick together after the collision.
 Calculate the speed of the car and truck after the collision   **[6]**

....

....

....

....

....

[Total = 9]

Exam practice questions

3   Roller coaster track:

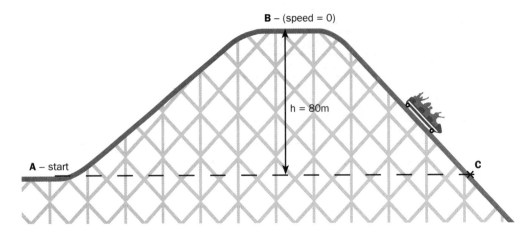

The mass of a car is 800 kg

Gravitational field strength = 10 N/kg

Assume there are no energy losses due to friction as the car goes round the track.

(a)   Calculate the increase in potential energy when the car moves from A to B.   **[2]**

....

....

(b)   What is the kinetic energy at point C? Explain how you know this.   **[2]**

....

....

(c)   Calculate the speed of the car at point C.   **[2]**

....

....

(d)   At the end of the ride, the kinetic energy of the car is 25 000 J. It brakes to a stop in 10 m. What is the braking force?   **[2]**

....

....

[Total = 8]

4   This van has a mass of 2000 kg.

Driving force   Resistive force
5000N

Exam practice questions

When the van travels at a steady speed of 30 m/s the resistive force is 5000 N.

(a) What is the driving force on the van? [1]

....

(b) Calculate the kinetic energy of the van. [2]

....

....

[Total = 3]

5 This table shows the shortest stopping distances for a car at different speeds.

Speed mph	Thinking distance (m)	Braking distance (m)	Stopping distance (m)
20	6	6	12
40	12	24	
60	18	55	73

(a) Work out the missing value for the stopping distance at 40 mph and write it in the table. [1]

(b) These are the shortest stopping distances. Describe some factors that will increase the stopping distance and explain whether each factor increases the thinking distance, or the braking distance. *The quality of your written communication will be assessed in this answer.* [6]

....

....

....

....

....

....

(c) In a collision test when a dummy hits the windscreen it stops in 0.001 s.

When the dummy is wearing a seatbelt it stops in 0.02 s.

(i) What happens to the seatbelt to make the stopping time longer? [1]

....

(ii) Explain why the longer stopping time reduces the damage to the dummy. [2]

....

....

[Total = 10]

10 Electricity

The following topics are covered in this chapter:

- Electrostatic effects
- Uses of electrostatics
- Electric circuits
- Voltage or potential difference
- Resistance and resistors
- Special resistors
- The mains supply

10.1 Electrostatic effects

LEARNING SUMMARY

After studying this section, you should be able to:

- Recall that electric charge can be positive or negative.
- Describe how objects can become charged.
- Describe forces between charged objects.
- Explain how objects are earthed.
- Explain some dangers and annoying effects of electric charge.

Electric charge

AQA	P2	✓
OCR A	P5	✓
OCR B	P4	✓
EDEXCEL	P2	✓

Electric charge can be **positive** or **negative**. **Electrons** are particles with a negative electric charge. They can move freely through a **conductor**, for example any type of metal, but cannot move through an **insulator**.

Two objects attract each other if one is positively charged and the other is negatively charged. Two objects with similar charge (both positive or negative) repel.

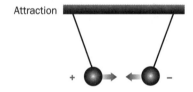
Attraction

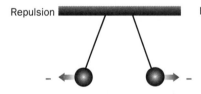
Repulsion

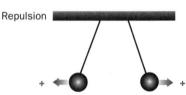
Repulsion

Electrostatic effects are caused by the transfer of electrons. (It is also sometimes called static electricity.) When insulators are rubbed, electrons are rubbed off one material and transferred to the other.

A polythene rod rubbed with a duster picks up electrons from the duster and becomes negatively charged, leaving the duster positively charged.

The insulated rod and the cloth have opposite charge.

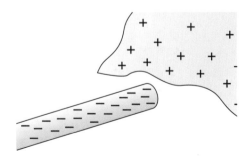

> **KEY POINT**
>
> Like charges repel. Unlike charges attract.

A Perspex rod rubbed with a duster loses electrons to the duster and becomes positively charged, leaving the duster negatively charged.

Materials that are positively charged have missing electrons. Materials that are negatively charged have extra electrons.

Charging and discharging

AQA	P2	✓
OCR A	P5	✓
OCR B	P4	✓
EDEXCEL	P2	✓

Conductors cannot be charged unless they are completely surrounded by insulating materials, such as dry air and plastic, otherwise the electrons flow to or from the conductor to discharge it.

An **insulated conductor** can be charged by rubbing it with a duster, or touching it with a charged rod. Some electrons are transferred, so that the charge is spread out over both objects.

A conductor can be discharged by touching it with another conductor, for example a wire, so that electrons can flow along the wire and cancel out the charge.

> Remember that it is the electrons that move from one object to another.

To stop conductors becoming charged they can be **earthed**. A thick metal wire is used to connect them to a large metal plate in the ground. This acts as a large reservoir of electrons. Electrons flow so quickly to, or from, earth that objects connected to earth do not become charged.

Dangerous or annoying?

AQA	P2	✓
OCR B	P4	✓
EDEXCEL	P2	✓

The human body conducts electricity. When a large flow of charge affects our nerves and muscles we call this an **electric shock**.

- Small electrostatic shocks are not harmful.
- Larger shocks can be dangerous to people with heart problems because a flow of charge through the body can stop the heart.
- Lightning is a very large electrostatic discharge. When it flows through a body it is often fatal.

Charged objects, like plastic cases and TV monitors, attract small particles of dust and dirt. Clothing can be charged as you move and 'clings' to other items of clothing, or the body. Synthetic fibres are affected more than natural fibres as they are better insulators. On a dry day charge can build up on you. When you touch metal, for example a car door, the charge flows from you to the metal, and you get a shock. A **spark** occurs when electrons jump across a gap. This can cause an explosion if there are:

Inflammable vapours like petrol or methanol

Inflammable gases like hydrogen or methane

Powders in the air, like flour or custard, which contain lots of oxygen – as a dust they can explode

Discharging safely

AQA	P2	✓
OCR B	P4	✓
EDEXCEL	P2	✓

Lorries containing flammable gases, liquids and powders are connected to earth before loading or unloading. Aircraft are earthed before being refuelled. This prevents charge from building up on metal pipes or tanks when the loads are moved, so there is no danger of a spark igniting the load.

Anti-static sprays, liquids and cloths stop the buildup of static charge. These work by increasing the amount of conduction, sometimes by attracting moisture because water conducts electricity.

If you stand on an insulating mat, or wear shoes with insulating soles, when you touch a charged object this will reduce the chance of an electric shock because the charge will not flow through you to earth. You become charged and stay charged until you touch a conductor.

PROGRESS CHECK

1. Why is a plastic rod attracted to a cloth it has been rubbed with?
2. What particles are transferred when a balloon is rubbed with a cloth?
3. How many types of electric charge are there?
4. Why do you become charged walking on a nylon carpet, but not on a woollen carpet?
5. When a plastic rod and a Perspex rod are both charged by rubbing they attract each other.
   a) What does this tell you about the charges on them?
   b) Would you expect two rubbed polythene rods to attract or repel?
6. Why are aircraft earthed before being refuelled?

6. So that there is not a build up of charge which could cause a spark. A spark would ignite the fuel.
5. a) They are opposite b) repel because they are the same, and would get the same charge.
4. Nylon is a better insulator. Some of the charges are conducted away through the wool carpet.
3. Two – positive and negative
2. Electrons
1. They have opposite charges, which attract.

10.2 Uses of electrostatics

LEARNING SUMMARY

After studying this section, you should be able to:

- Describe and explain some uses of electrostatics, including:
  - electrostatic precipitators
  - electrostatic paint spraying
  - defibrillators.

Electrostatic precipitators

OCR B   P4   ✓

Electrostatic precipitators remove dust or smoke particles from chimneys, so that they are not carried out of the chimney by the hot air.

An electrostatic precipitator.

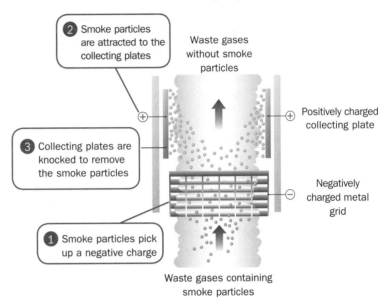

- Charged metal grids are put in the chimneys.
- The smoke particles pass through the grids and become charged.
- Plates at the side are oppositely charged to the grids.
- The smoke particles are attracted and stick to the plates.
- The smoke particles clump together on the plates to form larger particles.
- The plates are knocked and the large particles fall back down the chimney into containers.

> When you are describing how these applications work, explain what happens to the electrons in each case and how this affects the charge on the objects.

The grids are connected to a high voltage. They attract or repel charges in the smoke particles, so the particles become charged. The grids are positively charged in some designs and negatively charged in others. If the grids are positively charged, the plates are earthed. The smoke or dust particles lose electrons and become positively charged. They induce a negative charge on the earthed metal plate and are attracted to the plate. If the grids are negatively charged the plates are positively charged. The smoke or dust particles gain electrons and become negatively charged. They are attracted to the positively charged metal plates.

Spray painting

OCR B   P4   ✓
EDEXCEL P2   ✓

Before spray painting, the paint and the object are given different charges so that the paint is attracted to the object.

- The spray gun is charged so that it charges the paint particles.
- The paint particles repel each other to give a fine spray.
- The object is charged with the opposite charge to the paint.
- The object attracts the paint.
- The paint makes an even coat, it even gets underneath and into parts that are in shadow.
- Less paint is wasted.

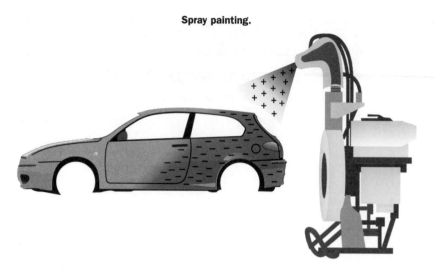

Spray painting.

In the example shown in the diagram, the paint droplets have lost electrons, so they are positively charged. The metal door panel is either connected to earth, or to a negative terminal so it is negatively charged. The positively charged drops are attracted to the negatively charged door. The door does not lose its negative charge, so it continues to attract positive droplets. As the coat of paint builds up, the new droplets will be attracted to the parts of the door that are the most negative – those in the shadows and cracks that the paint would not usually reach.

Crop spraying

| OCR B | P4 | ✓ |
| EDEXCEL | P2 | ✓ |

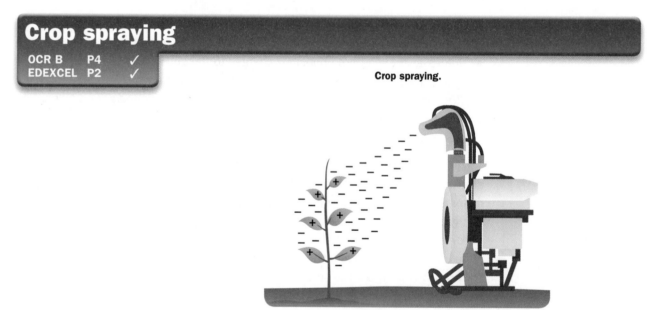

Crop spraying.

Fertiliser and insecticide spray nozzles are charged so that the droplets leaving the nozzle are charged. They repel each other and they are attracted to uncharged objects like the plants. The fine droplets cover the plant better and do not collect into large drops. They are less likely to drift in the wind and get wasted. This means that much less is used, which saves money and is better for the environment.

Defibrillators

OCR B   P4   ✓

When the heart beats, the heart muscle contracts. A **defibrillator** is used to start the heart when it has stopped.

The dotted lines show the path of the charge through chest, and heart.

- Two electrodes called paddles are placed on the patient's chest.
- The paddles must make a good electrical contact with the patient's chest.
- Everyone including the operator must 'stand clear' so they don't get an electric shock.
- The paddles are charged.
- The charge is passed from one paddle, through the chest to the other paddle to make the heart muscle contract.

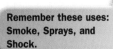

Remember these uses: Smoke, Sprays, and Shock.

The paddles take a few moments to charge up and then the discharge happens quickly. The electrons move through the heart muscle. Often the heart has not stopped, but has lost its steady rhythm. The defibrillator allows the heart to restart beating to its normal rhythm again.

PROGRESS CHECK

1. Why do the plates in the electrostatic precipitator have the opposite charge to the grids?
2. What would happen if the paint drops had the same charge as the car body?
3. Give an advantage of electrostatic crop spraying.
4. Why is it important to make sure no one except the patient gets a shock from a defibrillator?
5. Why are the grids in an electrostatic precipitator connected to a high voltage?
6. What would happen if the car door was not connected to earth or a negative charge?

1. The grids will attract (or repel) electrons from the smoke particles, which will be left with the same charge as the grid, so the plates need to have the opposite charge to attract the charged smoke particles.
2. They would be repelled and would not stick to the car body.
3. Better coverage or less wastage.
4. The shock could stop their heart.
5. So that they will charge the smoke particles that come close to them, by attracting or repelling electrons.
6. The positive drops would give the car body a positive charge so that eventually the car body would be positively charged and the paint would be repelled.

10.3 Electric circuits

LEARNING SUMMARY

After studying this section, you should be able to:

- Recognise circuit symbols.
- Draw electric circuits.
- Describe how to use an ammeter.
- Explain how charge flows in series and parallel circuits.
- Calculate electric charge and currents in circuits.

Circuit symbols

AQA   P2   ✓
OCR A   P5   ✓
EDEXCEL P2   ✓
WJEC   P2   ✓

To learn the symbols, draw or print them onto cards – one card with the word and one card with the symbol. Then use them to play 'pairs.' Place them face down and turn two over at a time. If you get a 'pair' of the matching word and symbol you keep it. If not you place them face down again. The winner is the person with the most pairs.

Component	Symbol	Component	Symbol
switch (open)		lamp	
switch (closed)		fuse	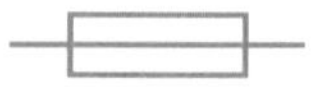
cell	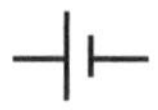	fixed resistor	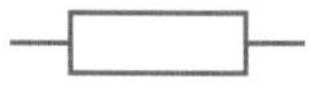
battery		variable resistor	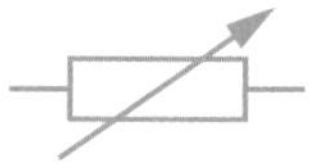
ammeter		light dependent resistor (LDR)	
voltmeter		thermistor	
junction of conductors		diode	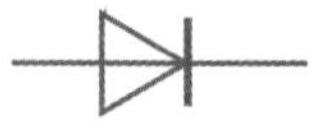
motor		generator	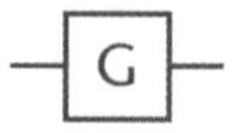
power supply		a.c. supply	

Take care when drawing circuit diagrams. Although the shape of the connecting wires does not matter they must join the components properly – electricity can't flow through gaps. The ammeter and voltmeter symbols are circles, not squares, and the symbol is 'A' not 'a'.

Electric current

AQA	P2	✓
OCR A	P5	✓
OCR B	P4	✓
EDEXCEL	P2	✓
WJEC	P2	✓

Electric current:

- is a flow of **electric charge**.
- only flows if there is a compete circuit. Any break in the circuit switches it off.
- is measured in **amps** (A) using an **ammeter**.
- is not used up in a circuit. If there is only one route around a circuit the current will be the same wherever it is measured.
- transfers energy to the components in the circuit.

A **series circuit** is a circuit with only one route around it. The current measured on each ammeter will be the same.

A series circuit.

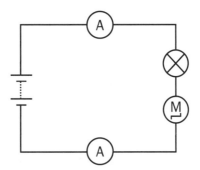

A **parallel circuit** has more than one path for the current around the circuit. In this circuit there are two paths, marked in red and blue, around the circuit. The current measured on ammeters B and C adds up to give the current measured on ammeter A and on ammeter D.

A parallel circuit.

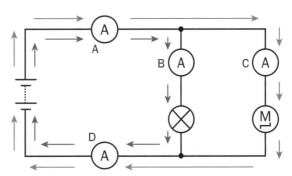

Electric current is a flow of **positive charge** so the direction of the current is opposite to the direction of the electron flow, because electrons are negatively charged.

> **KEY POINT**
>
> Electric charge is measured in **coulombs** (C). The amount of electric charge passing a point in the circuit depends on the current:
>
> **Charge (C) = current (A) × time (s)**
>
> $Q = I\,t$

Metal conductors contain lots of electrons that are free to move. When the battery makes the electrons move, they flow in a continuous loop around the circuit. In insulators there are few charges that are free to move.

> **KEY POINT**
>
> Batteries supply direct current, (d.c.) so the charges always move in the same direction from the positive terminal, around the circuit to the negative terminal. Mains electricity is produced by generators and the charges reverse direction. This is called alternating current (a.c.)

At a junction in a circuit, the total current flowing into the junction must be the same as the total current flowing out of the junction.

> **PROGRESS CHECK**
>
> 1. In the series circuit with two ammeters on page 191, if they both read 0.2 A what would be the reading on a third ammeter placed between the lamp and the motor?
> 2. In the parallel circuit on page 191, if ammeter B reads 0.3 A and ammeter C reads 0.5 A what is the reading on:
>   a) Ammeter A?
>   b) Ammeter D?
> 3. In the parallel circuit on page 191, if ammeter B reads 500 mA and ammeter A reads 900 mA what is the reading on:
>   a) Ammeter C?
>   b) Ammeter D?
> 4. If a current of 2 A is switched on for 10 s, how much charge has flowed?
> 5. In the parallel circuit on page 191, what will always be true about the readings on ammeters A, B and C?
>
> 5. reading A = reading B + reading C
> 4. 20 C
> 3. a) 400 mA b) 900 mA
> 2. a) 0.8 A b) 0.8 A
> 1. 0.2 A

10.4 Voltage or potential difference

LEARNING SUMMARY

After studying this section, you should be able to:
- Describe how to use a voltmeter.
- Explain and use the term potential difference.
- Use the relationships between potential difference, work and charge.
- Calculate voltages in series and parallel circuits.

Voltage or potential difference

AQA	P2	✓
OCR A	P5	✓
EDEXCEL	P2	✓
WJEC	P2	✓

KEY POINT

Voltage is also called **potential difference (p.d)**. Voltage is:

- Measured between two points in a circuit.
- Measured in **volts** (V) using a **voltmeter**.

The higher the voltage of a battery the greater the 'push' on the charges in the circuit.

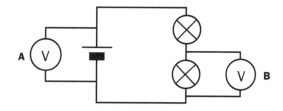

Students often confuse voltmeters and ammeters. Always say 'voltage across' and 'current through'.

This will remind you that to measure the current flowing through a component you must connect the ammeter in line, so that the current flows through it. To measure the voltage across the component you must connect the voltmeter across the component making a connection on either side of it.

This diagram shows how to connect voltmeter A to measure the voltage supplied by the battery, and how to connect voltmeter B to measure the voltage across one of the lamps.

Potential difference, or voltage, is a measure of energy transferred to (or from) the charge moving between the two points.

In the diagram:

- Voltmeter A is measuring the energy transferred *to* the charge.
- Voltmeter B is measuring the energy transferred *from* the charge.

Remember that 'a volt is a joule per coulomb.' Add to this that 'a coulomb is an amp second' and you can work out most of the electricity relationships you need.

KEY POINT

The potential difference (voltage) between two points is the work done (energy transferred) per coulomb of charge that passes between the two points.

$$\text{Potential difference (V)} = \frac{\text{Work done (J)}}{\text{Charge (C)}}$$

$$V = \frac{W}{Q}$$

Voltage in series or parallel

AQA	P2	✓
OCR A	P5	✓
EDEXCEL	P2	✓
WJEC	P2	✓

When components are connected in **series** the voltage, or p.d., of the power supply is shared between the components.

Adding the measurements on the three voltmeters gives the power supply p.d.

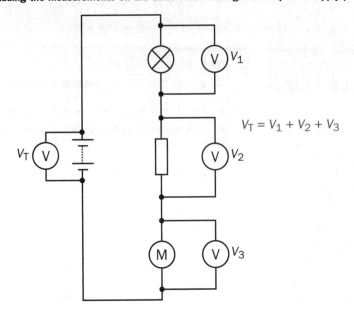

$$V_T = V_1 + V_2 + V_3$$

The measurements on all the voltmeters are the same.

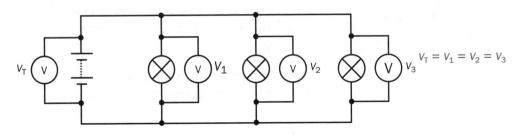

$$V_T = V_1 = V_2 = V_3$$

When components are connected in **parallel** to a power supply, the voltage, or p.d., across each component is the same as that of the power supply.

Connecting cells together

AQA	P2	✓
OCR A	P5	✓
EDEXCEL	P2	✓

Only identical cells should be connected together. In series the p.d. will be the sum of the p.d.s of the cells. In parallel, the p.d. is unchanged. The current will be larger when the cells are in series. In parallel, the current is unchanged, but the cells will last longer because there is more stored charge.

Cells connected in series and in parallel.

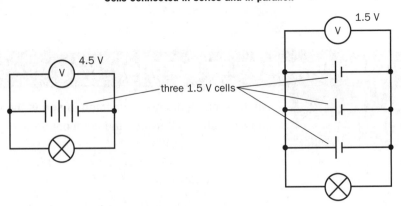

1 A motor, a resistor and a lamp are connected in series. The battery voltage is 12 V, the voltage across the motor is 6 V and across the resistor is 4 V.
   a) What is the voltage across the lamp?
   b) Does this mean that the current will be different in each component? Explain your answer.

2 In the parallel circuit on page 194 (middle), if the battery voltage is 9 V:
   a) what is the voltage across each of the lamps?
   b) Does this mean that the lamps will be equally bright? Explain your answer.

3 If the voltage across a lamp is 9 V and 10 C of charge flows through the lamp how much energy has been transferred?

4 What voltage would be supplied by five 1.5 V cells:
   a) in series?
   b) in parallel?

5 What advantage is there to connecting the five cells in parallel?

5. They will last longer – there is five times as much stored charge.
4. 2.a) 5 × 1.5 V = 7.5 V b) 1.5 V
3. 9 V × 10 C = 90 J
2. a) 9 V
   b) Yes, if the lamps are identical they will be equally bright. If they are different they might draw different current and have different brightness.
1. a) 2 V
   b) No, current is the same everywhere in a series circuit.

10.5 Resistance and resistors

LEARNING SUMMARY

After studying this section, you should be able to:

- Describe the effect of resistance.
- Use the relationship between resistance, current and voltage.
- Explain scientists' model of resistance in metals.
- Explain and use Ohm's Law.
- Calculate the total resistance of combinations of resistors.

Resistance

AQA	P2	✓
OCR A	P5	✓
OCR B	P4	✓
EDEXCEL	P2	✓
WJEC	P2	✓

The components and wires in a circuit **resist** the flow of electric charge. When the **voltage** (or p.d.), V, is fixed, the larger the **resistance** of a circuit the less **current**, I, passes through it.

The resistance of the connecting wires is so small it can usually be ignored. Other metals have a larger resistance, for example the filament of a light bulb has a very large resistance. Metals get hot when charge flows through them. The larger the resistance the hotter they get. A light bulb filament gets so hot that it glows.

For OCR B you need to know that resistance is the gradient of a V–I graph.

KEY POINT

Resistance is measured in **ohms** (Ω).

Resistance (Ω) = $\dfrac{\text{voltage (V)}}{\text{current (A)}}$

$R = \dfrac{V}{I}$

A model of resistance

| AQA | P2 | ✓ |
| OCR A | P5 | ✓ |

Metals are made of a **lattice** of stationary **positive ions** surrounded by **free electrons**. The moving electrons form the current. In metals with low resistance the electrons require less of a 'push' (p.d) to get through the lattice. The moving electrons **collide** with the stationary ions and make them **vibrate more**. This increase in kinetic energy of the lattice increases the temperature of the metal.

Free electrons   Lattice of positive ions

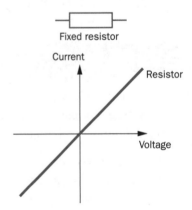

Fixed resistors

AQA	P2	✓
OCR A	P5	✓
EDEXCEL	P2	✓
WJEC	P2	✓

In some components, such as **resistors** and **metal conductors**, the resistance stays constant when the current and voltage change, providing that the temperature does not change. For this type of fixed resistance if the voltage is increased the current increases so that a graph of current against voltage is a straight line. The current is **directly proportional** to the voltage – doubling the voltage doubles the current. Components that obey this law (**Ohm's Law**) are sometimes called **ohmic** components.

When there is no voltage there is no current, so graphs of I against V pass through the point (0, 0). Remember this when you are drawing graphs.

A graph of current against voltage for a resistor.

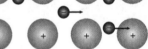

Fixed resistor

Current

Resistor

Voltage

Combining resistors

| AQA | P2 | ✓ |
| OCR A | P5 | ✓ |

Components can be added to a circuit in series or in parallel:

Resistors connected in series and parallel.

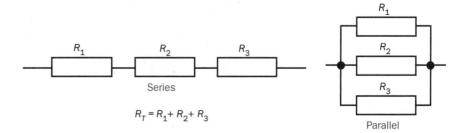

$$R_T = R_1 + R_2 + R_3$$

Series

Parallel

> A series is one after the other, parallel lines are side by side, so series circuits have one component after another and parallel circuits have components that can be drawn side by side instead of one after the other.

For components in series:

- Two (or more) components have more resistance than one on its own.
- The current is the same through each component.
- The p.d. is largest across the component with the largest resistance.
- The p.d.s across the components add up to give the p.d. of the power supply.
- The resistances of all the components add up to give the total resistance of the circuit.

For components in parallel:

- Two (or more) components have less resistance than one on its own.
- The current through each component is the same is if it were the only component.
- The total current will be sum of the currents through all the components.
- The p.d. across all the components will be the same as the power supply p.d.
- The current is largest through the component with the smallest resistance.

For components in **series**:

- Two (or more) components in series have more resistance than one on its own. This is because the battery has to push charges through both of them.
- The p.d. is largest across the component with the largest resistance. This is because more work is done by the charge passing through a large resistance than through a small one.

For components in **parallel**:

- A combination of two (or more) components in parallel has less resistance than one component on its own. This is because there is more than one path for charges to flow through.
- The current is largest through the component with the smallest resistance. This is because the same battery voltage makes a larger current flow through a small resistance than through a large one.

1. Lamp voltage = 9 V, current = 0.1 A. What is the resistance?
2. Voltage = 12 V, resistance = 200 Ω. What is the current?
3. In the series circuit on page 197 R_1 =100 Ω, R_2 = 200 Ω, R_3 = 300 Ω.
   a) What is the total resistance?
   b) Which resistor will have the largest voltage across it?
4. In the parallel circuit on page 197 R_1 = 100 Ω, R_2 = 200 Ω, R_3 =300Ω. Which resistor will have the largest current through it?
5. Why do metals get hot when an electric current flows through them?
6. A student takes these measurements for a resistor:
   $V = 3$ V $I = 20$ mA
   $V = 4.5$ V $I = 30$ mA
   Explain whether or not the resistor obeys Ohm's Law.

1. 90 Ω
2. 0.06 A
3. a) 600 Ω b) R_3 =300 Ω
4. R_1 = 100 Ω
5. The free electrons collide with the stationary positive ions giving them energy so they vibrate more, which means they are hotter.
6. Yes because V/I = 150 Ω in each case, so R is constant when V and I change, V is proportional to I.

10.6 Special resistors

After studying this section, you should be able to:

- Describe how resistance changes with temperature in thermistors and filament lamps.
- Describe how resistance changes with illumination for an LDR
- Describe the resistance of a diode and a variable resistor.
- Explain how these components can be used in circuits.

A filament lamp

AQA	P2	✓
OCR A	P5	✓
EDEXCEL	P2	✓

The wire in a **filament lamp** gets hotter for larger currents. This increases the resistance so the graph of current against voltage is not a straight line.

A graph of current against voltage for a filament lamp.

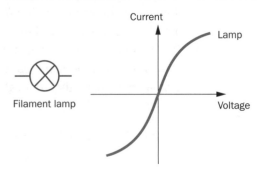

Filament lamp

Special resistors

AQA	P2	✓
OCR A	P5	✓
OCR B	P4	✓
EDEXCEL	P2	✓
WJEC	P2	✓

A **variable resistor** changes the current in a circuit by changing the resistance. This can be used to change how circuits work. For example to change:

- How long the shutter is open on a digital camera.
- The loudness of the sound from a radio loud speaker.
- The brightness of a bulb.
- The speed of a motor.

Inside one type of variable resistor is a long piece of wire made of metal with a large resistance (called **resistance wire**.) To alter the resistance of the circuit a sliding contact is moved along the wire to change the length of wire in the circuit.

The resistance of a **light dependent resistor (LDR)** decreases as the amount of light falling on it increases. It can be used in a circuit to switch a lamp on, or off, when it gets darker, or lighter.

A graph of resistance against intensity of light for an LDR.

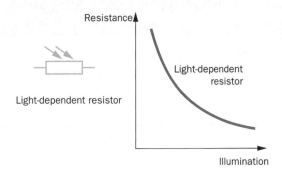

Light-dependent resistor

> When an ordinary resistor gets hotter its resistance increases, but for most common thermistors, resistance decreases. When light intensity increases LDRs resistance decreases. The extra energy makes it easier for current to flow in these materials.

The resistance of the most common type of **thermistor** (a negative temperature coefficient (NTC) thermistor) decreases as the temperature increases. It can be used in a circuit to switch a heater or cooling fan, on, or off, at a certain temperature.

A graph of resistance against temperature for a thermistor.

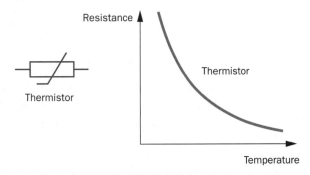

Thermistor

Diodes and LEDs

AQA	P2	✓
EDEXCEL	P2	✓

Current will only flow through a **diode** in one direction – the forward direction. In one direction its resistance is very low, but in the other direction, called the **reverse direction**, its resistance is very high.

A **light emitting diode (LED)** is a diode that emits light. LEDs are becoming widely used as low voltage and low energy sources of light.

Notice that symbols for diodes and LEDs (and also LDRs) sometimes include a circle.

LED.

A graph of current against resistance for a diode.

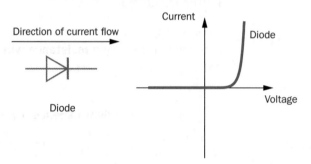

Direction of current flow

Diode

Current

Diode

Voltage

Using thermistors and LDRs

OCR A   P5   ✓

Two resistors can be used in a circuit to provide an **output p.d.** with the value that is wanted from a higher **input p.d.** This is called a **potential divider** circuit.

current: $I = \dfrac{V_{in}}{(R_1 + R_2)} = \dfrac{V_1}{R_1} = \dfrac{V_2}{R_2}$

voltage: $V_{in} = V_1 + V_2$

A potential divider circuit.

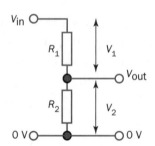

The p.d.s (or voltages) are divided in the same ratio as the resistances.

When a thermistor is used as one of the resistors, the resistance will change with the temperature. This circuit will produce a p.d. that changes with temperature and so it can be used to switch a heater on or off.

An LDR can be used in the same way.

a) The temperature dependent potential divider. b) A light dependent potential divider.

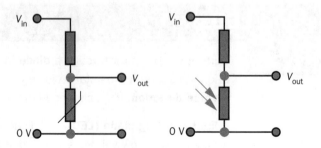

1. Why is the resistance of a filament lamp higher when it is switched on?
2. Why would the metal used to make lamp filaments be unsuitable for connecting components in a circuit?
3. What property of a thermistor makes it useful for controlling a heater?
4. Mains electricity is a.c. and computers require a d.c. supply. Which component would be useful in a circuit to connect a computer to use mains electricity? Why?
5. In the potential divider circuit on page 200 if the input p.d. $V_{in} = 5$ V, $R_1 = 200$ Ω and $R_2 = 300$ Ω. What is:
   a) V_1
   b) V_2
6. In the circuit with the thermistor on page 200 when the temperature increases what happens to:
   a) The resistance of the thermistor?
   b) The p.d. across the thermistor?
   c) The p.d. across the resistor?

6. a) decreases b) decreases c) increases.

b) $V_2 = 5$ V $\times \dfrac{300\ \Omega}{(300\ \Omega + 200\ \Omega)} = 3$ V or 5 V $- 2$ V $= 3$ V

5. a) $V_1 = 5$ V $\times \dfrac{200\ \Omega}{(300\ \Omega + 200\ \Omega)} = 2$ V

4. A diode – it only allows current to pass in one direction.
3. Its resistance decreases when temperature increases.
2. It has too high resistance and would get hot when current flowed.
1. Its temperature increases and so resistance increases.

10.7 The mains supply

LEARNING SUMMARY

After studying this section, you should be able to:

- Describe the mains electricity supply in the UK.
- Recall the wiring code for a three-pin plug.
- Explain the role of the fuse and the earth wire.
- Explain the advantages of an RCCB compared to a fuse.
- Use the relationship between power, current, voltage and resistance.

Mains electricity

AQA	P2	✓
OCR A	P5	✓
OCR B	P4	✓

- Mains voltage is 230 V a.c.
- The direction of the current and voltage changes with frequency = 50 Hz
- An electric shock from the mains can kill.

The alternating voltage can be displayed on an **oscilloscope**. The diagram shows an a.c. mains voltage stepped down to 25 V peak voltage

The vertical axis is the voltage of the a.c. supply. One vertical division = 10 V

The horizontal axis is the time. One horizontal division is 10 ms.

The **period** is the time for 1 cycle = 20ms.

$$\text{frequency (Hz)} = \frac{1}{\text{period(s)}} = \frac{1}{20 \text{ ms}} = 50 \text{ Hz}$$

a.c. mains displayed on an oscilloscope

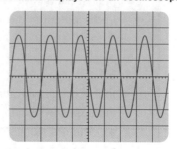

The colour code for mains electricity cables used in buildings and appliances is shown below.

Name of wire	Colour of insulation	Function of the wire
Live	Brown	Carries the high voltage.
Neutral	Blue	The second wire to complete the circuit.
Earth	Green and yellow	A safety wire to stop the appliance becoming live.

This diagram shows the wiring of a three-pin plug for a heater with a metal case. The **fuse** is always connected to the brown, **(live)** wire. A **cable grip** is tightened where the cable enters the plug to stop the wires being pulled out.

A three–pin plug on an earthed appliance.

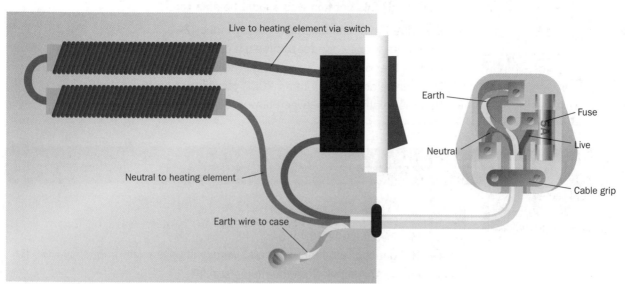

Live to heating element via switch

Earth

Fuse

Neutral

Live

Neutral to heating element

Earth wire to case

Cable grip

A **fuse** is a piece of wire that is thinner than the other wires in the circuit. If too much current flows it will melt before the wires overheat.

A 3 A fuse will melt if a current of 3 A flows through it. Choose a fuse that is greater than the normal operating current, but as low as possible. If there is a fault, or if too many appliances are plugged into one socket, resulting in a large current, then the fuse will melt and break the circuit preventing a fire.

The **earth wire** is connected to the metal case of appliances so that when they are plugged into the mains supply the metal case is earthed (see page 185.). If there is a fault and the live wire touches the metal case, a very large current flows through the low-resistance path to earth, melting the fuse wire and breaking the circuit.

Double insulated appliances have cases that do not conduct (usually plastic) and have no metal parts that you can touch, so they do not need an earth wire.

Residual current circuit breakers

| AQA | P2 | ✓ |
| OCR B | P4 | ✓ |

The **fuse** takes a short time to melt. It will not prevent you from getting an electric shock if you touch a live appliance. A residual current circuit breaker **(RCCB)** is safer.

Try explaining these safety features to someone. You'll soon find out if you remember them.

These are switches that cut off the electricity very quickly if they detect a difference in the current flowing in the live and the neutral wires, (for example, if the current flows through a person, or appliance casing). Another advantage is that they can be switched back on once the fault is fixed, whereas a fuse must be replaced.

A RCCB can be part of a mains circuit in a building, or a plug-in device that goes between the appliance and the socket. Appliances that are dangerous include:

- those where the cable could get wet, or be cut, for example, lawn mowers and power tools.
- music amplifiers connected to a metal instrument that someone is playing.

Electrical power

AQA	P2	✓
OCR A	P5	✓
OCR B	P4	✓
EDEXCEL	P2	✓
WJEC	P2	✓

The power is the rate at which the power supply transfers electrical energy to the appliance. It is measured in watts (W).

$$\text{power (W)} = \frac{\text{energy (J)}}{\text{time (s)}}$$

Electrical power (W) = current (A) × voltage (V)

$P = IV$

Electrical energy (J) = current (A) × voltage (V) × time (s)

$E = IVt$

Example: What is the current in a 2.8 kW kettle?

Using $P = IV$

$I = P \div V$

$I = 2800 \text{ W} \div 230 \text{ V} = 12.2 \text{ A}$

Power and resistance

WJEC   P2   ✓

Another useful equation is:

Using $P = IV$ and $R = \dfrac{V}{I}$ so $V = IR$

$P = I \times (IR) = I^2R$

Power (W) = [current(A)]^2 × resistance (Ω)

$P = I^2R$

Check carefully which equations you are given in the exam and which you need to learn. Make sure you know where to find them on the exam paper. You may find the triangle method useful for rearranging equations.

PROGRESS CHECK

1. Sam replaces a fuse with a piece of high resistance wire. Why is this a bad idea?
2. The earth wire is not connected to a metal appliance. Why is this dangerous?
3. What is the current in:
   a) a 2.5 kW kettle.
   b) a 9 W lamp.
   c) a 300 W TV?
4. Fuses come in 3 A, 5 A and 13 A. Which would you use for each appliance in question 3?
5. Give two advantages of using an RCCB with outdoor Christmas lights.
6. Cables have 100 Ω resistance. Calculate the power wasted heating the cables when the current is:
   a) 0.5 A.
   b) 1 A.

6. a) (0.5 A)^2 × 100 Ω = 25 W b) (1 A)^2 × 100 Ω = 100 W
5. If they get wet/wires get cut/other fault the power supply will be cut off. When the fault is fixed the power can be switched back on without replacing the fuse.
4. a) 13 A b) 3 A c) 3 A
3. a) 2500 W ÷ 230 V = 10.9 A b) 9 W ÷ 230 V = 0.04 A c) 300 W ÷ 230 V = 1.3 A
2. If the appliance becomes live it won't melt the fuse, so someone touching it could get a fatal shock.
1. It won't melt if the current gets too high – other wires may melt first causing a fire.

Sample GCSE questions

1 A fan uses mains electricity.

(a) Complete this table that describes the mains electricity supply in the UK. **[3]**

	Mains electricity in the UK
Voltage	230 V
Frequency	50 Hz
a.c. or d.c. ?	a.c.

(b) What is the difference between a.c. and d.c. voltage? A diagram may help you answer. **[2]**

d.c. = direct current, a.c. = alternating current. The difference in the voltages is shown on these graphs.

The fan has a power rating of 2 kW. When it is switched on, electric current flows through the circuit.

(c) What is an electric current? **[1]**

It is a flow of electric charge.

(d) Calculate the electric current in the fan. **[2]**

$P = IV$ $P = 2000W$ $V = 230V$

$I = \dfrac{P}{V}$ current $= \dfrac{2000\text{ W}}{230\text{ V}} = 8.7$ A

Current = ...8.7.... A.

(e) The plug has a 13 A fuse. Harry says that a residual current circuit breaker (RCCB) is better. Explain how a fuse works and the advantages of an RCCB. *The quality of your written communication will be assessed in this answer.* **[6]**

A fuse is a thinner piece of wire than the rest of the circuit with a lower melting point. If the current in the circuit is too large the fuse will melt before the other wires and break the circuit. This will prevent overheating and fires, but it is too slow to prevent electric shocks. The advantages of the RCCB are that it will stop the current much faster than a fuse and it can be reset after the fault is fixed, whereas the fuse has to be replaced.

[Total = 14]

Graphs must have axes labelled 'voltage' and 'time'. Alternatively, write 'd.c. is direct current so the voltage is always in the same direction. a.c. is alternating current so the voltage keeps changing direction.' (Note: not just changing, but changing direction.)

Write down the equation and the values you are using. You may get marks. Use the value for voltage that you used in part (a) if it is incorrect you will not lose marks again – your answer here will be marked correct.

Marks will be awarded depending on the number of relevant points included in the answer and the spelling, punctuation and grammar. In this question there are 8 or 9 relevant points so 7 or 8 including 2 advantages of RCCBs with good spelling punctuation and grammar will gain full marks.

Sample GCSE questions

2 Kate is investigating how the thickness of a piece of wire affects its resistance.

(a) Complete this circuit diagram to show how she should connect an ammeter and a voltmeter to measure the voltage across the wire and the current flowing through it. **[2]**

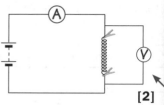

> You must use the correct circuit symbols, leave no gaps, and connect the voltmeter across the wire and the ammeter in line with it.

(b) Kate has a selection of wires of different thickness. State two factors that must be the same for all the test wires. **[2]**

1. *The length of the wire.*

2. *The metal the wire is made from.*

(c) Here are Kate's results.

Thickness of wire (mm)	Voltmeter reading (volts)	Ammeter reading (amps)	Resistance (ohms)
0.5	12.0	0.30	40
1.0	12.0	0.67	18
1.5	12.0	1.20	10
2.5	12.0	2.67	4.5
3.5	12.0	4.80	

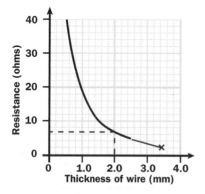

> Remember to include the unit of resistance, Ω or 'ohms' is OK for the mark.

(i) Calculate the resistance of the 3.5 mm thickness wire. **[2]**

$R = V/I$ $R = 12.0V \div 4.80A = 2.5\ \Omega$

Resistance = ...2.5Ω....

> The graph is a smooth curve so do not draw a straight line with a ruler. Use a pencil to continue the curve. Turn the paper if it helps. Do not make the line very thick or draw lots of attempts. Remember that exam papers are scanned and marked on screen, so a poorly erased line may still appear.

(ii) Plot your calculated value on the graph. **[1]**

(iii) Extend the line to include your plotted value. **[1]**

(d) Use the graph to find the resistance of a wire with thickness 2.0 mm. **[1]**

Resistance = ...6.5Ω....

[Total = 9]

Exam practice questions

1 Gemma uses an electrostatic paint spray to paint a metal fence. The spray nozzle gives the paint droplets a positive charge.

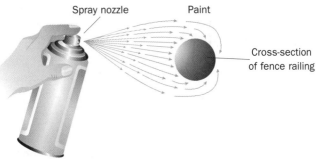

Spray nozzle   Paint

Cross-section
of fence railing

(a) The metal fence is given an electric charge. Explain whether this is a positive or negative charge. **[2]**

....

....

(b) Explain how charging the paint and the fence improves the paint spraying process. *The quality of your written communication will be assessed in this answer.* **[6]**

....

....

....

....

....

[Total = 8]

2 Explain how a defibrillator is used to restart the heart. *The quality of your written communication will be assessed in this answer.* **[6]**

....

....

....

....

3 A car headlamp uses a 12 V battery.

(a) 300 C of charge pass through the bulb in 1 minute. Calculate the current in the lamp. **[2]**

....

....

Exam practice questions

(b) Calculate the energy transferred to the lamp by 300 C of charge flowing through it. **[2]**

....

....

(c) Calculate the power of the lamp. **[2]**

....

....

[Total = 6]

4 Sadia has bought a new electric lamp. It is double insulated so it does not need earthing.

(a) What does double insulated mean? **[1]**

....

(b) The lamp has a 3 A fuse. Describe what happens when **[2]**

(i) the normal current of 0.25 A flows in the circuit.

....

(ii) there is a fault and the current increases to 5 A.

....

(c) The fault is fixed and the fuse is replaced with a 13 A fuse. Explain why this is not a good idea. **[2]**

....

....

[Total = 5]

5 A mains electricity fan heater has two switches (mains is 230 V).

Switch X turns the fan motor on and off. Switch Y turns the heater on and off.

(a) Label the switches X and Y on the circuit diagram. **[1]**

(b) Is it possible to turn the heater on without the fan? .... **[1]**

(c) Is it possible to turn the fan on without the heater? .... **[1]**

(d) Explain why the switches have been arranged to work in this way. **[3]**

....

....

....

Exam practice questions

(e) The resistance of the motor is 70 Ω. Calculate the current in the motor. **[3]**

....

....

(f) The current in the heater is 0.6 A. What is the total current from the power supply? **[3]**

....

....

[Total = 12]

6 This diagram shows a circuit that can be used to control a lighting circuit.

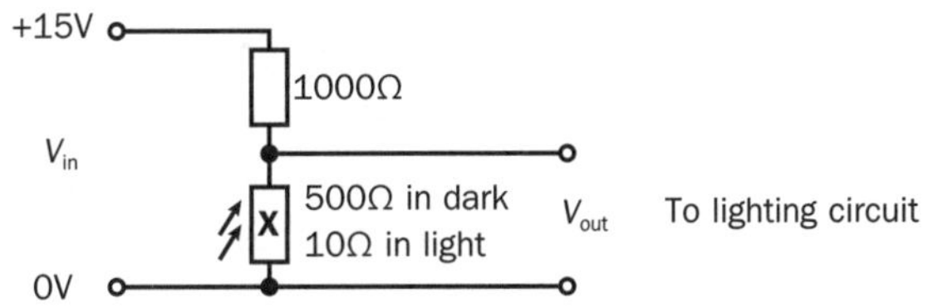

+15V
1000Ω
V_{in}
500Ω in dark
10Ω in light
X
V_{out} To lighting circuit
0V

(a) What is the name of the component marked X in the circuit? **[1]**

....

(b) In the dark, what is the total resistance of the circuit? **[1]**

....

(c) In the dark, what is the potential difference: **[2]**

(i) across the 1000 Ω resistor? ....

(ii) across the component marked X? ....

(d) Describe what happens to the resistance and the potential difference across component X as the light level changes. *The quality of your written communication will be assessed in this answer.* **[6]**

....

....

....

(e) Explain how this could be used to control the lighting circuit. **[2]**

....

....

[Total = 9]

11 Radioactivity

The following topics are covered in this chapter:

- **Atomic structure**
- **Radioactive decay**
- **Living with radioactivity**
- **Uses of radioactive material**
- **Nuclear fission and fusion**

11.1 Atomic structure

LEARNING SUMMARY

After studying this section, you should be able to:

- Describe the atom and the particles it is made of.
- Write symbols for nuclei.
- Complete nuclear equations for alpha and beta decay.
- Describe, and explain the results of, Rutherford's gold foil experiment.

The atom

AQA	P2	✓
OCR A	P6	✓
OCR B	P4	✓
EDEXCEL	P2	✓
WJEC	P2	✓

Atoms are about 10^{-10} m or 0.1 nanometres in diameter. Neutral atoms have the same number of protons and electrons. When ionisation occurs atoms gain or lose electrons, becoming negatively or positively charged **ions**.

KEY POINT

- The **atom** is mostly empty space with almost all the mass concentrated in the small positively charged nucleus at the centre.
- The nucleus is very small compared to the volume, or shell, around the nucleus that contains the **electrons**.

A model of the atom.

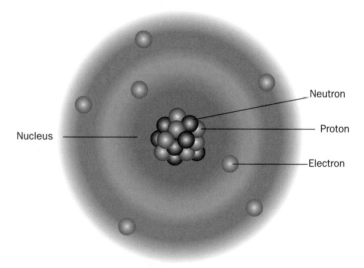

Nucleus — Neutron — Proton — Electron

Particles in the atom	Symbol	Where found in the atom	Relative mass	Relative charge
Proton	p	In nucleus	1	+1
Neutron	n	In nucleus	1	0 (neutral)
Electron	e	Outside nucleus	$\dfrac{1}{1840}$	−1

Make a set of flash cards with these words on one side and what they mean on the other. Keep looking at them and this will help you remember them.

> **KEY POINT**
>
> The **nucleus** of an atom contains particles called **protons** and **neutrons**. These are also called **nucleons**.
>
> The **atomic number** or **proton number**, Z, is the number of protons in the nucleus.

The number of protons is what makes the atom into the element it is, so, for example, hydrogen always has one proton and carbon always has six.

> **KEY POINT**
>
> The **mass number** or **nucleon number**, A, is the total number of protons and neutrons in the nucleus.
>
> **Isotopes** of an element have the same number of protons in the nucleus, but different numbers of neutrons. This means that different isotopes of an element each have the same proton or atomic number but a different nucleon or mass number.

Isotopes of the same element have exactly the same chemical properties, but they have different mass and nuclear stability. For example, carbon-12 is a stable isotope of carbon with 6 protons and 6 neutrons and carbon-14 is a radioactive isotope with 6 protons and 8 neutrons.

Nuclear equations

AQA	P2	✓
OCR A	P6	✓
OCR B	P4	✓
EDEXCEL	P2	✓
WJEC	P2	✓

Nuclei are given symbols, for example, this is the symbol for the stable isotope carbon-12 which has 6 protons and 6 neutrons:

$$^{12}_{6}\text{C}$$

This is the symbol for an alpha particle (see page 213), which is the same as a helium nucleus. Sometimes α is used instead of He:

$$^{4}_{2}\text{He}$$

A beta particle (see page 213) is not a nucleus, but this symbol is used for a beta particle in a nuclear equation. Sometimes β is used instead of e:

$$^{0}_{-1}\text{e}$$

> **KEY POINT**
>
> Before and after a nuclear decay or reaction:
>
> - The total of the mass numbers must be the same.
> - The total of the atomic numbers must be the same.

Example: Alpha decay of radon-220.

$$^{220}_{86}\text{Rn} \rightarrow {}^{216}_{84}\text{Po} + {}^{4}_{2}\text{He}$$

$220 = 216 + 4$ and $86 = 84 + 2$

Example: Beta decay of carbon-14.

$$^{14}_{6}\text{C} \rightarrow {}^{14}_{7}\text{N} + {}^{0}_{-1}\text{e}$$

$14 = 14 + 0$ and $6 = 7 + (-1)$

A model of the atom

OCR A   P6   ✓

Before 1910 scientists had a **plum pudding model** of the **atom**. In this model the atom is described as being made of positively charged material (the pudding) with negatively charged electrons (the plums) inside.

> This is an example of how scientists change their ideas over time.

Later Ernest Rutherford investigated the structure of atoms by firing **alpha particles** at **gold foil**. He suggested the **nuclear model** of the atom.

What happened to the alpha particles	Ernest Rutherford's explanation – the nuclear atom
The majority went straight through the foil, without being deflected.	The atom is mostly empty space.
Some were deflected and there was a range deflection angles.	Parts of the atom have positive charge.
A very small number were 'back-scattered' – they came straight back towards the alpha particle source.	There is a tiny region of concentrated mass and positive charge which repels the very small number of alpha particles that have a head-on collision.

The experiment was carried out in a vacuum, so that the alpha particles were not stopped by the air. A fluorescent screen flashed each time an alpha particle hit it. The location of each flash showed whether the alpha particle had travelled straight through the foil or whether it had been deflected. Hans Geiger and Ernest Marsden counted small flashes of light under the direction of Ernest Rutherford. The experiment is often referred to as Rutherford scattering.

Alpha particle scattering by gold foil.

> Remember: Most straight through, some deflected, very few straight back.

11.2 Radioactive decay

LEARNING SUMMARY

After studying this section, you should be able to:

- Describe the properties of alpha, beta and gamma emissions.
- Explain that radioactive decay is random.
- Explain and calculate half-life.
- Understand the term 'activity' in relation to a radioisotope.
- Interpret decay curves of isotopes.

Alpha, beta and gamma

AQA	P2	✓
OCR A	P6	✓
OCR B	P4	✓
EDEXCEL	P2	✓
WJEC	P2	✓

There are three main types of radioactive emissions: **alpha particles**, **beta particles** and **gamma rays**. This table shows some of the properties of the different types of radiation.

Radiation	Ionising effect	Electric charge	Stopped by ...	Affected by electric and magnetic fields?
Alpha (α)	Strong	+	Skin. A few cm of air. A sheet of paper.	Yes
Beta (β)	Weak	−	A thin sheet of aluminium or other metal.	Yes
Gamma (γ)	Very weak	Neutral	A thick lead sheet reduces intensity. Thick concrete blocks reduce intensity.	No

When alpha and beta particles are emitted the nucleus changes into a different element. When gamma rays are emitted the element does not change.

KEY POINT

Alpha emission is when two protons and two neutrons leave the nucleus as one particle, called an **alpha particle**. An alpha particle is identical to a helium nucleus.

Beta emission is when a neutron decays to a proton and an electron inside the nucleus. The high energy electron leaves the nucleus as a **beta particle**.

Gamma emission is when the nucleus emits a short burst of high-energy **electromagnetic radiation**. The **gamma ray** has a high frequency and a short wavelength.

| Alpha particle (α) | Beta particle (β) | Gamma rays (γ) |

Radioactive decay

AQA	P2	✓
OCR A	P6	✓
OCR B	P4	✓
EDEXCEL	P2	✓
WJEC	P2	✓

KEY POINT

A radioactive material contains nuclei that are unstable and emit nuclear radiation. This process is called **radioactive decay**. Radioactive decay is **random**.

It is not possible to predict when it will happen, nor is it possible to make it happen by a chemical or physical process, for example by heating the material. A radioactive source contains millions of atoms. The number of radioactive emissions a second depends on two things:

• The type of nucleus – some combinations of protons and neutrons are more stable than others.
• The number of undecayed nuclei in the sample – with double the number of nuclei, on average, there will be double the number of emissions per second.

Over a period of time the **activity** of a source gradually reduces.

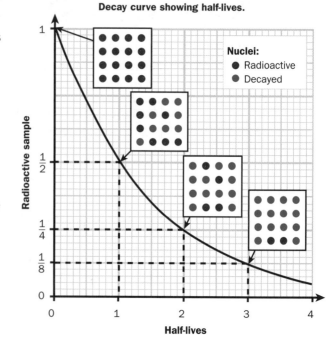

Decay curve showing half-lives.

Nuclei:
● Radioactive
● Decayed

The **half-life** of an isotope is the average time taken for half of the nuclei present to decay.

Example: Technetium-99m (Tc-99m) decays by gamma emission to Technetium-99 (Tc-99) with a half-life of six hours. After six hours, only half of the Tc-99m nuclei remain. After another six hours, that is a total of 12 hours, only one quarter are left.

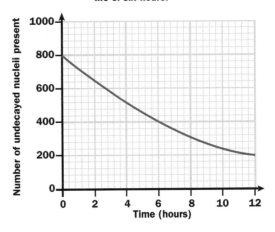

The decay of a sample radioactive nuclei with a half-life of six hours.

This pattern is the same for all isotopes, but the value of the half-life is different. Carbon-14 has a half-life of 5730 years; some isotopes have a half-life of less than a second.

Activity

The number of radioactive emissions a second is called the **activity** of the source. On average, in one half-life the activity of a source will reduce to one half of its original value.

After this number of half-lives ...	The activity has dropped to this fraction of the initial value ...	Which is the same as ...
1	$\frac{1}{2}$	$\frac{1}{2^1}$
2	$\frac{1}{2} \times \frac{1}{2} = \frac{1}{4}$	$\frac{1}{2^2}$
3	$\frac{1}{2} \times \frac{1}{2} \times \frac{1}{2} = \frac{1}{8}$	$\frac{1}{2^3}$
10	$\frac{1}{1024}$	$\frac{1}{2^{10}}$

Common mistakes are to say:
- After three half-lives there are 1/3 or 1/6 of the radioactive nuclei left – but it is 1/8.
- '1/8 of the nuclei have decayed' – but it is 7/8 because only 1/8 are left.

After ten half-lives, the activity has dropped to less than one thousandth of the original activity. This is often used as a measure of the time for a sample to decay to a negligible amount.

For a source with a half-life of 2 hours, after 20 hours the activity is ...

20 hours ÷ 2 hours = 10 half-lives

Fraction of original activity = $\frac{1}{2^{10}}$ = 1/1024

PROGRESS CHECK

1. Answer alpha, beta or gamma to the following.
   a) Which type of radiation has a positive charge?
   b) Which types of radiation can be stopped by a thin sheet of aluminium?
   c) Which type of radiation passes through a sheet of paper and is deflected by a magnet?

PROGRESS CHECK

2 A radioactive source has a half-life of 24 hours. What fraction will remain after **a)** one day and **b)** four days?

3 Describe what happens to an alpha particle as it passes through acid.

4 A radioactive source with a half-life of three hours has an activity of 16 000 Bq. What is the activity after:

a) 3 hours?

b) 9 hours?

c) 30 hours?

d) When will the activity be 500 Bq?

1. a) alpha particle
   b) alpha particles and beta particles
   c) beta
2. a) ½ b) 1/16
3. It loses energy as it slows down and attracts 2 electrons, becoming a helium atom.
4. a) $16\ 000 \div 2 = 8000$ Bq b) $16\ 000 \div 2^3 = 2000$ Bq c) $16\ 000 \div 2^{10} = 16$
   d) $16\ 000$ Bq $\times \frac{1}{2} \times \frac{1}{2} \times \frac{1}{2} \times \frac{1}{2} \times \frac{1}{2} = 500$ Bq $= 5$ half lives $= 5 \times 3$ hours $= 15$ hours

11.3 Living with radioactivity

LEARNING SUMMARY

After studying this section, you should be able to:

- Understand and explain the term background radiation.
- Describe some sources of background radiation.
- Explain the difference between contamination and irradiation.
- Understand the term radiation dose.
- Describe the different risks of α, β and γ exposure.

Background radiation

AQA	P2	✓
OCR A	P6	✓
OCR B	P4	✓
EDEXCEL	P2	✓

Some radioactive materials occur naturally, others are man-made. **Cosmic rays** from space make some of the carbon dioxide in the atmosphere radioactive. The carbon dioxide is used by plants and enters food chains. This makes all living things radioactive. Some rocks are naturally radioactive.

KEY POINT

We receive a low level of radiation from these sources all the time. It is called **background radiation**.

Background radiation comes from:

- Radon (a radioactive gas) from rocks.
- Soil and building materials.
- Medical and industrial uses of radioactive materials.
- Food and drink.
- Cosmic rays (from outer space).
- 'Leaks' from radioactive waste and nuclear power stations.

Background radiation in the UK.

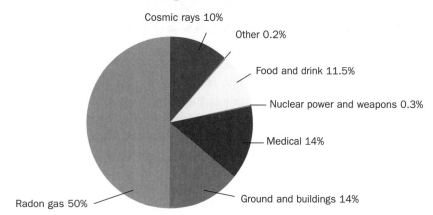

Background radiation in the UK.

Cosmic rays 10%

Other 0.2%

Food and drink 11.5%

Nuclear power and weapons 0.3%

Medical 14%

Ground and buildings 14%

Radon gas 50%

> Sources of background radiation: cosmic rays are from outer space (not the Sun).
>
> Food and drink are radioactive as explained on page 216 – not because of food irradiation.

Some rocks are more radioactive than others, so the level of background radiation can depend on the underlying rocks. In certain areas, **radon** from some rocks can build up in houses. It emits alpha radiation, so it is particularly damaging in the lungs. Houses with high levels of radon can have under-floor fans fitted to keep the radon out of the house.

In some parts of the country the rocks are more radioactive than in others and there is a higher level of background radiation.

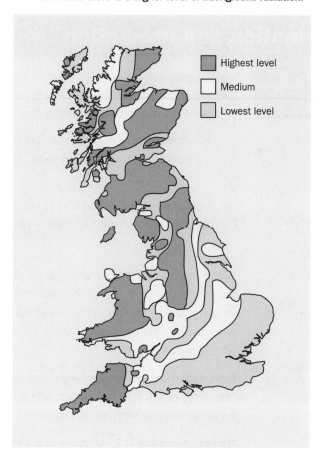

Highest level

Medium

Lowest level

> Background radiation is the name given to radioactive emissions from nuclei in our surroundings. Do not confuse this with radiation from mobile phones or cosmic microwave background radiation.

Dangers of radiation

AQA   P2   ✓
OCR A   P6   ✓
OCR B   P4   ✓
EDEXCEL   P2   ✓

KEY POINT

Ionisation is when atoms gain or lose electrons becoming negatively or positively charged. **Ionising radiation** is radiation that has enough energy to ionise the atoms in molecules. The **ions** can take part in chemical reactions. In **living cells** this can damage or kill them. It can damage the **DNA** so that the cell **mutates** into a **cancer** cell.

It is not possible to predict which cells will be damaged by exposure to radiation or who will get cancer.

Scientists studied the survivors of incidents where people were exposed to ionising radiation. They measured the amount of exposure and recorded how many people later suffered from cancer. The risk of cancer increases with increased exposure to radiation. People tend to overestimate the risk from radiation because it is invisible and unfamiliar. They underestimate the risk of familiar activities, like smoking.

Contamination and irradiation

AQA   P2   ✓
OCR A   P6   ✓
OCR B   P4   ✓
EDEXCEL   P2   ✓

KEY POINT

There are two types of danger from radioactive materials.

- **Irradiation** is exposure to radiation from a source outside the body.
- **Contamination** is swallowing, breathing in, or getting radioactive material on your skin.

A short period of irradiation is not as dangerous as being contaminated because, once contaminated, a person is continually being irradiated.

Alpha radiation has very short range. Even if it reaches the skin it does not penetrate, so there is little danger from irradiation. However, it is strongly ionising, so contamination by an alpha source, for example breathing in radon gas, can be very dangerous. Once inside the lungs it will keep irradiating sensitive cells.

Beta radiation has longer range and penetrates the skin so there is more danger from irradiation. It is not as strongly ionising as alpha, so contamination is not as dangerous as with alpha radiation.

Gamma radiation is long range and passes right through the body. There is a danger from irradiation if the radiation levels are high. It is only weakly ionising and most of the rays pass right through the body without hitting anything so contamination is less dangerous than with alpha or beta radiation.

Radiation dose

OCR A   P6   ✓

Radiation dose, measured in **sieverts** (Sv), is a measure of the possible harm done to the body. Radiation dose depends on the type of radiation, the time of exposure, and how sensitive the tissue exposed is to radiation. The dose is linked to the risk of cancer developing. Alpha radiation is strongly ionising and so the dose is twenty times larger from alpha than from beta or gamma radiation.

The normal UK background dose is a few milliSieverts. A fatal dose is between 4 Sv and 5 Sv given in one go.

PROGRESS CHECK

1. Give a source of background radiation.
2. How much of the background radiation in the UK is from radon gas?
3. Give one effect of ionising radiation on living cells.
4. 'She has been irradiated, she will get cancer.' What is wrong with this statement?
5. Name a part of the UK that has high background radiation.

5. e.g. Cornwall, Cumbria, other orange areas on map
4. Her risk of getting cancer is increased, but we can't tell whether she will get cancer.
3. kill, damage, damage DNA, turn cancerous
2. 50% (or half)
1. One of sources on piechart on page 217, e.g. cosmic rays (outer space)

11.4 Uses of radioactive material

LEARNING SUMMARY

After studying this section, you should be able to:

- Explain whether alpha, beta or gamma radiation is the most suitable to use.
- Choose the most suitable radioisotope for a job.
- Describe how radioisotopes are used.
- Consider benefits and risks in the use of radioactive isotopes.

Choosing the best isotope

AQA   P2   ✓
OCR A   P6   ✓
OCR B   P4   ✓
EDEXCEL   P2   ✓
WJEC   P2   ✓

Radioactive materials can be useful as well as harmful. When a radioactive material is to be used certain factors need to be considered.

- Alpha, beta or gamma radiation is chosen depending on the **range** and the **absorption** required.
- An isotope is chosen depending on:
  - whether it emits alpha, beta or gamma radiation
  - how long it remains radioactive, which depends on the half-life.

Radioactive isotopes for different uses are produced in nuclear reactors.

Medical tracers

AQA	P2	✓
OCR A	P6	✓
OCR B	P4	✓
EDEXCEL	P2	✓
WJEC	P2	✓

Isotopes which emit **gamma radiation** (or sometimes **beta radiation**) are used in **medical tracers**. The patient drinks, inhales, or is injected with the tracer, which is chosen to collect in the organ doctors want to examine.

Example: Radioactive iodine is taken up by the thyroid gland, which can then be viewed using a **gamma camera** that detects the gamma radiation passing out of the body. The tracer must not decay before it has moved to the organ being investigated, but it must not last so long that the patient stays radioactive for weeks afterwards.

Treating cancer

AQA	P2	✓
OCR A	P6	✓
OCR B	P4	✓
EDEXCEL	P2	✓
WJEC	P2	✓

Isotopes which emit a higher dose of **gamma radiation** than tracers are used to build up in the cancer and kill the cancer cells. Alternatively, beams of **gamma rays** are concentrated on a tumour to kill the cancer cells.

Example: Cobalt-60 emits high energy gamma rays and remains radioactive for years.

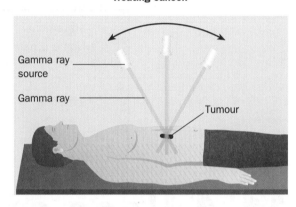

Treating cancer.

Gamma ray source

Gamma ray

Tumour

Benefits and risks

AQA	P2	✓
OCR A	P6	✓
OCR B	P4	✓
EDEXCEL	P2	✓
WJEC	P2	✓

When radioactive materials are used, we have to decide whether the **benefits** outweigh the **risks**.

Example: Treatment benefits patients, but does not benefit hospital staff who work with radioactive materials regularly.

Radiation workers have their exposure monitored and take safety precautions to keep their dose as low as possible:

- They wear protective clothing.
- They keep a long distance away, for example they use tongs to handle sources.
- They keep the exposure time short.
- They shield sources and label them with

> Use a mnemonic that contains the first letters of each to remember safety precautions: <u>M</u>y <u>c</u>urtains <u>d</u>im the <u>b</u>right <u>l</u>ight
>
> <u>M</u>onitor, <u>c</u>lothing, <u>d</u>istance, <u>t</u>ime, <u>b</u>arrier, <u>l</u>abel.

Radioactive hazard symbol.

Sterilisation

AQA	P2	✓
OCR A	P6	✓
OCR B	P4	✓
EDEXCEL	P2	✓
WJEC	P2	✓

Gamma radiation destroys microbes and is used for:

- Sterilising equipment, for example surgical instruments.
- Food irradiation to extend the shelf-life of perishable food.

The food or equipment does not become radioactive because it is only **irradiated**, there is no **contamination**. It is irradiated inside the plastic packaging, so that it stays sterile.

Smoke detectors

OCR B	P4	✓
EDEXCEL	P2	✓

Isotopes which emit **alpha radiation** are used in **smoke detectors**. The alpha radiation crosses a small gap and is picked up by a detector. If smoke is present, the alpha radiation is stopped by the smoke particles. No radiation reaches the detector and the alarm sounds.

Beta and gamma radiation are unsuitable because they pass through the smoke.

Tracers

OCR B	P4	✓
EDEXCEL	P2	✓

Isotopes which emit beta radiation or gamma radiation can be used as tracers. Because a tracer is radioactive, detectors can track where it goes. A tracer can be added to sewage at an ocean outlet, or as it enters a river, to trace its movement. In this way, leaks in power station heat exchangers can be tracked. The isotope used has an activity that will fall to zero quickly after the test is done.

Thickness detectors (gauging)

EDEXCEL	P2	✓

Isotopes which emit beta radiation are used in thickness detectors.

Example: Some of the beta radiation is absorbed by a paper sheet. If the sheet is too thick, less beta radiation is detected and the pressure of the rollers is increased. If the sheet is too thin, more beta radiation is detected and the pressure is reduced.

Using a beta source to control paper thickness.

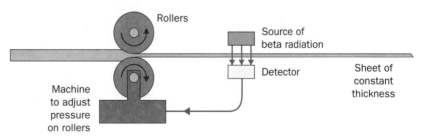

Carbon dating

OCR B	P4	✓
WJEC	P2	✓

The amount of radioactive carbon left in old materials that were once living can be used to calculate their age.

Carbon dating:

- Can only be used for things that once lived.
- Cannot be used for objects older than 10 half-lives = 10 × 5730 years or less than 100 years.

Carbon dating.

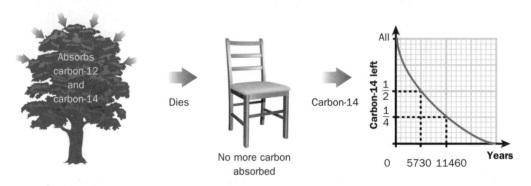

Some rocks contain a radioactive isotope of uranium that decays to lead, so they can be dated by comparing the amounts of uranium and lead. The more lead there is the older the rock is.

Learn the properties of alpha, beta and gamma radiation, so that you can explain why each is chosen.

PROGRESS CHECK

1. Give a use of:
   a) Alpha radiation.
   b) Beta radiation.
   c) Gamma radiation.
2. Explain why healthy tissue is not killed by the gamma rays from the cobalt-60 during cancer treatment.
3. Why are alpha and gamma radiation not suitable for gauging the thickness of paper?
4. Why is carbon dating not used to confirm the age of a 60 000 year-old egg?

4. There is no radioactive carbon left in the egg, so it could be much older – you can't tell.
3. Alpha is all absorbed by paper, gamma will all pass through the paper.
2. Each of the beams in the diagram is a low dose so it doesn't kill the cells, but when combined in the tumour the dose is high enough to kill the cells.
c) e.g. cancer treatment
b) e.g. medical tracer
1. a) e.g. smoke detector

11.5 Nuclear fission and fusion

<table>
<tr><td rowspan="2">**LEARNING SUMMARY**</td><td>**After studying this section, you should be able to:**</td></tr>
<tr><td>

- Describe nuclear fission.
- Recall $E = mc^2$.
- Describe how chain reactions are used in nuclear reactors.
- Describe how nuclear waste is disposed of.
- Describe nuclear fusion.
</td></tr>
</table>

Nuclear fission

AQA	P2	✓
OCR A	P6	✓
OCR B	P4	✓
EDEXCEL	P2	✓
WJEC	P2	✓

KEY POINT

Nuclear fission is when a nucleus splits into two nuclei of about equal size, and two or three neutrons.

Example: After uranium-235 absorbs a neutron:

A neutron absorbed by a uranium nucleus causes a nuclear fission.

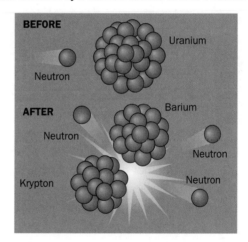

$E = mc^2$

| OCR A | P6 | ✓ |

KEY POINT

A small amount of mass is converted into a large amount of energy. The energy is calculated using Einstein's equation:

Energy (J) = mass (kg) × speed of light in a vacuum (m/s)^2

$E = mc^2$

About a **million times more energy** is released than in a chemical reaction.

A chain reaction

AQA	P2	✓
OCR A	P6	✓
OCR B	P4	✓
EDEXCEL	P2	✓
WJEC	P2	✓

KEY POINT

After the new neutrons slow down, they can strike more uranium nuclei and cause more fission events. This is called a **chain reaction**.

A chain reaction.

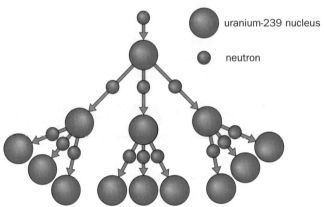

○ uranium-239 nucleus

○ neutron

If the chain reaction runs out of control it is an **atomic bomb**. In a **nuclear reactor** the process is controlled. In a nuclear power station the energy released is used to generate electricity.

Nuclear reactors

AQA	P2	✓
OCR A	P6	✓
OCR B	P4	✓
EDEXCEL	P2	✓
WJEC	P2	✓

In a nuclear reactor:

- The **fuel rods** are made of **uranium-235** or **plutonium-239**.
- The **moderator** is a material that slows down the neutrons.
- The energy heats up the reactor core.
- A **coolant** is circulated to remove the heat.
- The hot coolant is used to heat water to steam, to turn the power station turbines.
- The **control rods** are moved into the reactor to absorb neutrons to slow or stop the reaction.

Nuclear reactor.

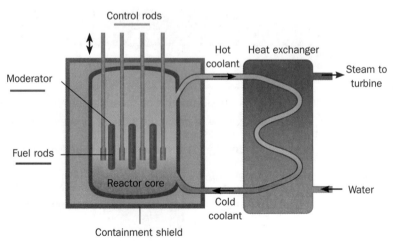

Waste disposal

OCR A	P6	✓
OCR B	P4	✓
EDEXCEL	P2	✓

Reactors produce **radioactive waste**. The half-life of some isotopes is thousands of years, so radioactive waste must be kept safely contained for thousands of years.

> You may be asked for advantages and disadvantages, for example, of methods of waste disposal or nuclear reactors. To gain full marks you must give at least one advantage *and* one disadvantage.
>
> If you are asked for your opinion it doesn't matter if you say 'yes' or 'no', but you must say one or the other. Remember that most of the marks are for justifying your choice.

Types of radioactive waste	Examples	Disposal
Low level waste	Used protective clothing.	Sealed into containers. Put into landfill sites.
Intermediate level waste	Material from reactors.	Mixed with concrete. Stored in stainless-steel containers.
High level waste	Used fuel rods.	Kept under water in cooling tanks (it decays so fast it gets hot). Eventually becomes intermediate level waste.

Where is the safest place to store the radioactive waste?

- At the bottom of the sea, but the containers may leak.
- Underground, but the containers may leak and earthquakes or other changes to the rocks may occur.
- On the surface, but needs guarding from terrorists, for thousands of years.
- Blast into space, but there is a danger of rocket explosion.

Nuclear fusion

AQA	P2	✓
OCR A	P6	✓
OCR B	P4	✓
EDEXCEL	P2	✓
WJEC	P2	✓

When two small nuclei are close enough together they can **fuse** together to form a larger nucleus. This releases a large amount of energy.

> Draw up a table to compare fusion and fission. It will help you when you revise.

The problem is getting the two nuclei close enough, because nuclei are positively charged and **repel** each other. Inside stars the temperatures are high enough for the nuclei to have enough energy to get close enough for nuclear fusion to occur.

Scientific research is continuing to try and control the nuclear fusion reaction and produce nuclear fusion reactors. Advantages of a fusion reactor over a fission reactor would be:

- The reaction stops if there is a fault.
- There would be less radioactive waste.
- More energy would be produced.

The protons and neutrons inside the nucleus are held together by a force called the **strong force**.

The problem is getting, and keeping, the temperature and pressure high enough to overcome the repulsive force, so that the nuclei get close enough for the strong force to take over. When fusion happens a small amount of mass is converted into a large amount of energy ($E = mc^2$).

The ITER project is to build a fusion reactor in which hydrogen-1 and hydrogen-2 nuclei are fused to give helium-3 nuclei. It involves many scientists from 20 countries. Scientists work together because the project is so expensive and because they make more progress if they share ideas.

Cold fusion

AQA	P2	✓
OCR A	P6	✓
OCR B	P4	✓
EDEXCEL	P2	✓
WJEC	P2	✓

Fusion research and reactors are very expensive. Martin Fleischmann and Stanley Pons were scientists with a track record of success in other fields. In 1989 they announced that they had achieved nuclear fusion without high temperatures in a process called **cold fusion**.

They used a cheaper electrolysis experiment with a palladium and a platinum electrode in 'heavy water.' This is water made from the hydrogen isotope that has a neutron in the nucleus. A lot of heat was generated and they claimed to have detected neutrons showing that fusion had taken place.

Many scientists tried to **replicate** the experiment. Fleischmann and Pons released very few details, possibly because of the chance of a Nobel prize, or a patent being awarded. (If they released too many details someone else might get there first.) They had rushed to publish something because they thought one of the scientists who **peer reviewed** their request for research money might claim credit for their idea. Some scientists claimed to have replicated their experiment, and some could not. Eventually almost all the claims of success were retracted as careful checking showed the heat and neutrons were not due to nuclear fusion. Fleischmann and Pons could have brought more details of the experiment, or data as evidence, but they never did. Scientists assume they could not **reproduce** it.

The **peer review** process works best when scientists behave ethically and for the common good. Cold fusion is an example where the peer review process did not work well, because scientists did not share their results and ideas.

> This is an example of 'How Science Works' which is on all specifications, although the details of the cold fusion experiment are only required for OCR B and Edexcel.

> Even a scientist who usually shares their ideas may be afraid that others will not treat him, or her, the same way when there is money or a Nobel Prize at stake.

PROGRESS CHECK

1. What is the difference between nuclear fission and nuclear fusion?
2. Describe a chain reaction in plutonium-239.
3. Explain what control rods are used for.
4. How are fuel rods disposed of when the fuel is used up?
5. How much energy results from 0.1 g of fuel being converted to energy?
6. What is the force that holds protons and neutrons together?

1. Fission is splitting large nuclei into two roughly equal parts, fusion is joining two small nuclei.
2. The plutonium-239 nucleus absorbs a neutron splits into two parts and a few extra neutrons. These neutrons are absorbed by more plutonium-239 nuclei which split – and so on.
3. To absorb neutrons and stop them causing more nuclei to fission. The rods are lowered or raised to change the number of neutrons absorbed and control the rate of reaction.
4. Stored under water in cooling tanks (high level waste).
5. $0.1\ g = 0.0001\ kg \times (3 \times 10^8\ m/s)^2 = 9 \times 10^{12}$ J
6. The strong force.

Sample GCSE questions

1 This diagram shows a source of beta radiation used to control the thickness of paper produced by a factory manufacturing paper.

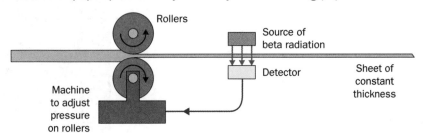

(a) What is beta radiation? **[2]**

Beta radiation is fast moving electrons emitted by radioactive nuclei when they decay.

There are two marks so you need to say more than 'electrons'

(b) Explain how the thickness of the paper is controlled. *The quality of your written communication will be assessed in this answer.* **[6]**

The beta radiation is directed from the source through the paper to the detector. Some of the radiation will be stopped by the paper. If the paper is too thin the amount of beta radiation passing through the sheet increases so a signal is sent to the rollers to decrease the pressure and make the sheet thicker. If the paper is to thick the amount of radiation reaching the detector will decrease so a signal is sent to the rollers to increase the pressure and make the sheet thinner.

Marks will be awarded depending on the number of relevant points included in the answer and the spelling, punctuation and grammar. In this question there are about 6 relevant points so 5 or 6 points with good spelling, punctuation and grammar will gain full marks.

(c) Why is alpha radiation or gamma radiation not used? **[2]**

Alpha radiation would all be absorbed by a thin sheet of paper and none would reach the detector. Gamma radiation is very penetrating and would all pass through a thick sheet of paper and reach the detector.

(d) The radioactive source used is strontium-90. Complete this equation for the radioactive decay of strontium-90 to the element yttrium. **[3]**

$$^{90}_{38}\text{Sr} \rightarrow {}^{90}_{39}\text{Y} + {}^{0}_{-1}\text{e}$$

Notice that you don't have to know anything about yttrium to complete the equation. The beta particle is represented as 'e'. Fill in mass number '0' and proton number of '−1' (because it has a charge of −1 and a proton is changed to a neutron when a beta particle is emitted) . To balance the equation the numbers for yttrium are 90 − 0 = 90 and 38 − (−1) = 39.

[Total = 13]

Sample GCSE questions

2 Radon-222 is a radioactive gas. This graph shows the radioactive decay of a sample of radon-222.

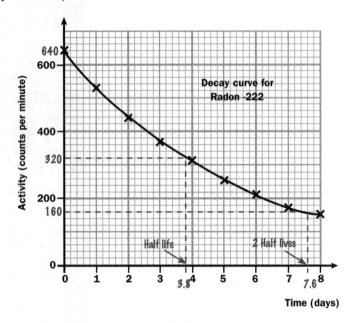

(a) Use the graph to find the half-life of radon-222 **[2]**

Half-life of radon-222 = ...3.8 days...

Radon-222 decays to polonium-218 by emitting an alpha particle.

(b) Complete this equation for the decay. **[3]**

$$^{222}_{86}Rn \rightarrow \,^{218}_{84}Po + \,^{4}_{2}He$$

Radon gas is a decay product from radioactive rocks in the Earth's crust. It contributes to about 50% of the background radiation in the UK.

(c) Explain what is meant by 'background radiation'. **[1]**

Background radiation is the low level of radiation from the radioactive decay of sources that are all around us all the time.

(d) In some parts of the country radon gas can build up in houses. Explain why this is a health hazard. *The quality of your written communication will be assessed in this answer.* **[4]**

The radon gas breathed into the lungs will decay by emitting alpha particles. Alpha particles are very ionising and when they irradiate the lung tissue the cells may be damaged or killed. If the DNA is damaged the cells may mutate and become cancerous.

[Total = 10]

Exam practice questions

1 **(a)** A patient is injected with Technetium-99 m which has a half-life of 6 hours. What fraction of the Technetium-99m nuclei are left after one day? **[1]**

....

(b) Why is it better to use an isotope with a half-life of 6 hours rather than:

(i) an isotope with a half-life of 6 minutes? **[1]**

....

(ii) an isotope with a half-life of 6 days? **[1]**

....

[Total = 3]

2 Read this information about radiation treatment for cancer.

To treat cancer of the thyroid gland patients are given a dose of iodine-131. Iodine is absorbed by the thyroid gland, so the radioactive iodine kills the cancer cells. After the treatment patients are radioactive for a few days. When the level drops to the normal background level patients can leave the hospital.

(a) Jack says he thought radiation caused cancer so how can radioactive iodine cure it? Explain how radiation can be both the cause and cure of cancer. **[3]**

....

....

....

(b) Sam has been treated for thyroid cancer. He says 'The benefit outweighed the risk'. Explain what he meant. **[2]**

....

....

Jo is a smoker. She avoided meeting Sam when he left hospital after being treated with a radioactive isotope because she was afraid Sam might be radioactive. Sam was not allowed to leave until his radioactivity level was below 3 mSv. He showed Jo the table below.

This table compares the risks of different activities by working out an average of days of life lost for each activity. This is worked out by:

$$\frac{\text{total days of life lost by all the people who died early}}{\text{total population}}$$

Exam practice questions

Activity	Average days/years lost
Smoking 20 cigarettes a day	6 years
All accidents	207 days
Cancer due to being exposed to 3 mSv of radiation	15 days
Cancer due to being exposed to 10 mSv of radiation	51 days

Sam said that Jo was more at risk from smoking than from any remaining radioactivity.

(c) Explain why Sam was correct. [2]

....

....

....

(d) Suggest why Jo was more worried about radioactivity than smoking. [1]

....

[Total = 8]

3 Factory waste is discharged from a pipe at sea. To check that it is not being washed up on a nearby beach, a radioactive tracer is added. A suitable isotope to use would be: [1]

A an alpha emitter with a half-life of 2 days

B a beta emitter with a half-life of 2 days

C a beta emitter with a half-life of 1 year

D a gamma emitter with a half-life of 1 year.

☐

4 Put these statements in order to describe how the age of a wooden spear is determined using carbon dating. The first has been done for you. [5]

A A sample of the wood is tested to find the proportion of carbon-14.

B The proportion of carbon-14 in the wood falls as the nuclei decay.

C Carbon dioxide, containing some carbon-14, is taken in by the living tree during photosynthesis.

D The tree is cut down and no more carbon-14 is taken in.

E The result is compared with living wood and only half of the carbon-14 is left.

F The wood is made into a spear.

G The age of the spear is one half-life, which is 5730 years.

C							

Exam practice questions

5 Match the descriptions with the type of nuclear waste by drawing one straight line from each box on the left to one box on the right. **[2]**

Description	Type of waste
Used fuel rods from nuclear reactors	High level waste
Protective clothing worn by workers	Intermediate level waste
Reactor fuel containers	Low level waste

6 **(a)** What is nuclear fission? **[1]**

....

(b) How does the energy produced by nuclear fission compare with that produced in a chemical reaction? **[1]**

....

(c) Write **T** for the **true** and **F** for the **false** statements below. **[5]**

(i) Nuclear reactors use fuel rods made of uranium-235 or plutonium-239. ☐

(ii) A chain reaction occurs when a nucleus splits and releases a few neutrons which can be absorbed by other nuclei and cause them to split. ☐

(iii) Control rods are lowered into the nuclear reactor core to speed up the reaction. ☐

(iv) The energy released when the nuclei split heats up the reactor core. ☐

[Total = 7]

7 Scientists are researching the process of nuclear fusion with the aim of producing a fusion reactor. Explain the nuclear fusion process. *The quality of your written communication will be assessed in this answer.* **[6]**

....

....

....

....

....

....

Answers

Note: For questions involving QWC, marks will be awarded if:
- All information in answer is relevant, clear, organised and presented in a structured and coherent format.
- Specialist terms are used appropriately.
- There are few, if any, errors in grammar, punctuation and spelling

Chapter 1

1. **(a)** Peter's gametes: X and Y.
   Correct offspring: XX, XX, XY, XY.
   (b) (i) All countries.
   All ratios after the age of 65 show less than one man to each woman.
   (ii) India.
   The ratio of boys to girls at birth is highest/above one to one.
   (iii) Imbalance in the sex ratio in the country leading to possible drop in population.

Chapter 2

1. **(a) (i)** $6O_2$; $6CO_2$
   (ii) Three from: to supply the body with more oxygen.
   Because respiration rate has increased in the muscles.
   To prevent anaerobic respiration.
   To remove the extra carbon dioxide.
   (b) glucose → lactic acid + energy
   (c) There is still excess carbon dioxide to be removed.
   Lactic acid has to be broken down.
   Payback the oxygen debt.
2. **(a)** The rate of reaction steadily increases as the temperature increases.
   Peaks at about 43°C.
   Above that the rate drops rapidly.
   (b) Three from: up to the optimum any increase in temperature increases the kinetic energy.
   Molecules collide more/collide with more energy.
   Above optimum the enzymes start to denature.
   Substrate cannot fit into active site.
   (c) Enzyme A is from the human because its optimum is closest to 37°C, body temperature.
   Enzyme B is from the bacterium as it can work at high temperatures.
3. **(a)** Three from: the two strands of DNA unwind and unzip.
   Each strand attracts complementary bases.
   The bases are joined together and each molecule winds up.
   Each new molecule has one old and one new strand.
   (b)

Feature	Mitosis	Meiosis
Number of cells made from one cell	**Two**	Four
Uses of cells that are made	Growth /repair / asexual reproduction	**Sex cells**
Number of chromosomes in the cells made	**Same number as the parent cells**	Half the number of the parent cell

   (c) In the first division the whole chromosomes from each pair move apart.
   In the second division the copies of each chromosome move apart.

Chapter 3

1. **(a) (i)** This is the place that organisms live, i.e. the pond.
   (ii) All the organisms of one species living in the pond.
   (iii) All the living organisms in the pond plus all the non-living components e.g. water and soil.
   (b) (i) A net.
   (ii) Area is $3.142 \times 7.5^2 = 176.74$ m^2.
   Population = $5 \times 176.74 = 884$ snails.
   (iii) $30 \times \frac{29}{2} = 435$ (1 mark for calculation and 1 mark for answer)
   (iv) The second method because it samples in 5 areas.
   One area might not be representative.
2. **(a) (i)** Tree gained 78 kg but soil only lost 1 kg.
   All the mass could not have come from the soil.
   (ii) Water is needed for photosynthesis.
   But so is carbon dioxide.
   And minerals are also needed from the soil.
   (b) Three from: he would use telephones; letters; scientific journals; lectures.
   van Helmont would not have used the telephone.
3. **(a) (i)** It may leave toxic residues/many kill pollinating insects/may kill predators of red spiders.
   (ii) Spider population is developing resistance.
   (b) (i) Biological control.
   (ii) Must make sure that the introduced organism; does not become a pest.
   (c) Hydroponics.
   Easy to provide the plant with minerals.
   Can include insecticide in the water.

Chapter 4

1. **(a)** It loses mass at a steady rate.
   Because it is losing water.
   (b) Lose less mass than the unpainted leaf because nail varnish prevents water loss.
   Less mass lost when bottom surface is painted because stomata are found there.
   Little difference if top surface painted as already a waxy cuticle present.
   (c) More wind movement causes more water loss.
   It blows away the water that has diffused out.
2. **(a)** Blood is pumped by the heart.
   It does carry oxygen to the tissues.
   However it returns in different vessels called veins.
   (b) The veins are carrying blood back to the heart from the arm and so blood gets trapped.
   (c) (i) Valves.
   (ii) The blood is under higher pressure in arteries so would not flow backwards.
   (d) Capillaries.
   His microscope was not powerful enough.
3. **(a) (i)** Absorption of digested food.
   (ii) Two from: large surface area/long.
   Villi/folds/microvilli.
   Rich blood supply.
   (b) (See QWC guidance on page 232.)
   Emulsifies fat.
   Increases the surface area of the droplets.
   Allows lipase to work faster.
   Neutralises acid from stomach.

Answers

Chapter 5

1. (a) 10
   (b) 20
   (c) (2, 8)
   (d) Period 2; Group 8
2. (a) 3
   (b) 5
   (c) It has lost; two electrons
   (d) 2–
3. (a) The transition or d-block
   (b) Metals
4. (a) $Mg(s) + Cl_2(g) \longrightarrow MgCl_2(s)$
   (b) $4Fe(s) + 3O_2(g) \longrightarrow 2Fe_2O_3(s)$
5. (a) They increase
   (b) It decreases
   (c) As you go down the group there are more electron shells; which shield the nucleus so it cannot attract electron
6. (a) The materials for the new drug could be rare or may require expensive extraction from plants.
   (b) You can make a product quickly on demand; You can make a product on a small scale; The equipment can be used to make a variety of products
7. (See QWC guidance on page 232.)
   Magnesium oxide would be solid at room temperature.
   Magnesium oxide would have a high melting point.
   Magnesium oxide would have a high boiling point.
   Because the attraction between magnesium ions and oxide ions is very strong.
   Ionic bonds are not easily broken.
   Magnesium oxide would conduct electricity when molten.
   Because melting frees the ions, allowing them to move.

Chapter 6

1. (a) Delocalised means not part of one particular atom
   (b) Electrostatic attraction; between positive ions and electrons
   (c) Electrical conductivity
2. (a) Hydrogen
   (b) Sodium hydroxide
   (c) $2Na + 2H_2O \longrightarrow 2NaOH + H_2$ (1 mark for formulae, 1 mark for balancing)
3. (a) The cation (metal ion) present in a salt
   (b) Sodium ions are present
   (c) Both give a green flame colour
   (d) The wire must be free from any salts previously tested; which might give false flame colours
4. (a) An acidified solution of silver nitrate
   (b) A precipitate is formed
   (c) Chloride gives a white precipitate; bromide gives a cream precipitate
   (d) $Ag^+(aq) + Cl^-(aq) \longrightarrow AgCl(s)$
5. (a) Known substances are tested to see if any of them are matches for the unknown substance.
   (b) detergent

Chapter 7

1. (a) By filtration
   (b) Evaporating the water
   (c) Copper(II) carbonate + sulfuric acid → copper(II) sulfate + water (1 mark for reactants, 1 mark for products)
   (d) The reaction is exothermic

2. (a) Sodium chloride
   (b) Hydrogen and chlorine
   (c) Sodium hydroxide
   (d) So they do not react with hydrogen, chlorine or sodium hydroxide
3. (a) Farmers apply nitrates to fields; which are washed into rivers by rainwater
   (b) Nitrates are all soluble in water
   (c) To kill bacteria
   (d) By limiting the amount applied to the fields

Chapter 8

1. (a) 100
   (b) 0.25 mol
   (c) 56
   (d) 44 g; 1 mole of carbon dioxide is lost as gas
2. (a) 48 g
   (b) 32 g
   (c) 80 g
   (d) $\dfrac{6}{24} = 0.25$ $0.25 \times 40 = 10$ g
3. (a) 550°C
   (b) 34%
   (c) The yield increases
4. (a) They must collide; with sufficient energy.
   (b) (i) B
       (ii) C
       (iii) The steeper slope is the faster reaction; Calculate the gradient
   (c) A collision must have enough energy for the particles to react; If they do not have sufficient energy they will not react.

Chapter 9

1. DBCEAF (1 mark for B anywhere before C, 1 mark for C anywhere before E, etc)
2. (a) 20m/s × 1200 kg = 24 000 kg m/s
   (b) C
   (c) Total momentum before = 24 000 kg m/s + 45 000 kg m/s = 69 000 kgm/s
       = total momentum after = (1200 kg + 3000 kg) × velocity.
       Velocity = 69 000 kgm/s ÷ 4200 kg = 16.4 m/s
3. (a) 800 kg × 10 N/kg × 80 m = 640 000 J
   (b) gain in KE = loss in PE = 640 000 J
   (c) 640 000J = ½ mv^2 = ½ × 800kg v^2 , v = √ (1600 m/s) = 40 m/s
   (d) 25 000 J ÷ 10 m = 2500 N
4. (a) steady speed, resultant force = 0, so force = 5000 N
   (b) ½ × 2000 kg × (30 m/s)^2 = 900 000 J
5. (a) 12 + 24 = 36
   (b) If the driver is tired, or affected by some drugs (including alcohol and some medicines), or distracted and not concentrating the time for him or her to react will be increased, during this time the car travels further so the thinking distance is increased.
       If the road is wet or icy, or the tyres or brakes are in poor condition, the friction forces will be less so the braking distance is increased.
       If the vehicle is fully loaded with passengers or goods the extra mass reduces the deceleration during braking, so the braking distance is increased.

Answers

Marks will be awarded depending on the number of relevant points included in the answer and the spelling, punctuation and grammar. In this question there are 6 relevant points so 5 or 6 points with good spelling punctuation and grammar will gain full marks.

(c) (i) It stretches

(ii) Force = change of momentum ÷ time (or rate of change of momentum) The momentum changes to zero when the dummy stops. The force on the dummy depends on the time this takes. If the time to stop is longer the force is smaller.

Chapter 10

1. (a) The fence is given a negative charge so that it attracts the positively charged paint drops.

(b) By giving the paint drops and the fence opposite charges the paint droplets will be attracted to the fence and repelled from each other so they will spread out evenly over the metal surface and even curve round to coat the back of the fence as shown in the diagram. This means that less paint will be wasted by falling on the ground or drifting away in the air and the paint coat will be even, and get in to hard to reach corners.

Marks will be awarded depending on the number of relevant points included in the answer and the spelling, punctuation and grammar. In this question there are about 6 relevant points so 5 or 6 points including two advantages will gain full marks.

2. Paddles are placed on the patient's chest. They must make a good electrical contact with the body. To make the heart muscle contract, electric charge is passed from one paddle to the other through the body. This starts the heart beating steadily again.

Marks will be awarded depending on the number of relevant points included in the answer and the spelling, punctuation and grammar. In this question there are 3 or 4 relevant points so 3 or 4 points with good spelling punctuation and grammar will gain full marks.

3. (a) current = charge ÷ time = 300 C ÷ 60 s = 5 A

(b) voltage = energy ÷ charge
energy = 12 V × 300 C = 3600 J

(c) $P = IV$ power = 5 A × 12 V = 60 W

4. (a) the case is a non-conductor

(b) (i) current flows normally

(ii) fuse melts and breaks the circuit.

(c) the fuse will not melt until 13A flows, this is a much higher current than needed and damage will be done before the fuse melts.

5. (a) left hand switch = X, right hand switch = Y.

(b) no

(c) yes

(d) You can switch on only the fan so that it can be used for cooling. You cannot switch on only the heater in order to prevent it from overheating. The air from the fan is needed to cool the heating element.

(e) 230 V ÷ 70 Ω = 3.3 A

(f) 3.3 A + 0.6 A = 3.9 A

6. (a) Light dependent resistor

(b) 1000 Ω + 500 Ω = 1500 Ω

(c) (i) (15 V ÷ 1500 Ω) × 1000 Ω = 10 V

(ii) (15 V ÷ 1500 Ω) × 500 Ω = 5 V

(d) As the light level increases the resistance decreases so the p.d. across the LDR decreases. (Although question says changes, you need to say increase and decrease in the answer.)

Marks will be awarded depending on the number of relevant points included in the answer and the spelling, punctuation and grammar. In this question there are 3 steps so all 3 points with good spelling, punctuation and grammar will gain full marks.

(e) As the light level increases the drop in p.d. could switch a light off, (or as the light level decreases the increase in p.d. could switch a light on).

Chapter 11

1. (a) one sixteenth

(b) (i) It would decay away before reaching the organ and being recorded by the gamma camera

(ii) the patient would stay radioactive for days.

2. (a) The radiation is ionizing so it can kill or damage cells. It can be used to kill cancer cells. If it damages healthy cells they can turn cancerous.

(b) The benefit of killing the thyroid cancer outweighed the risk of causing another cancer.

(c) The risk of being exposed to 3 mSV of radiation amounts to 15 days lost on average, but the risk from smoking amounts to 6 years lost on average, so smoking is much more dangerous.

(d) People are more worried about unfamiliar things and overestimate the risk.

3. B

4. CDFBAEG (1 mark for each of: D anywhere before F, similarly F before B, B before A, A before E, E before G.)

5. Fuel rods = high, protective clothing = low, fuel containers = intermediate.

6. (a) A nucleus splits into two parts of roughly equal size.

(b) A million times more in a nuclear reaction than a chemical reaction.

(c) (i) T

(ii) T

(iii) F

(iv) T

7. Nuclear fusion occurs when two light/small nuclei get close enough and join together to form a larger nucleus releasing a large amount of energy in the process. The energy is given by $E = mc^2$ (where m = mass and c = speed of light). The protons and neutrons in the nucleus are held together by the strong force. The difficulty is in getting the nuclei close enough for the strong force to take effect because the nuclei are positively charged and positive charges repel. The nuclei must be heated to a high temperature so they have a lot of kinetic energy. This is what happens in the Sun where hydrogen nuclei are fused to give helium nuclei.

Marks will be awarded depending on the number of relevant points included in the answer and the spelling, punctuation and grammar. In this question there are about 10 relevant points so 8 or 9 points with good spelling, punctuation and grammar will gain full marks.

Notes

Notes

Notes

Index

absorption 62
acceleration 159-162, 166-167
activation energy 140, 148
active transport 34
activity 214-215
adaptations 60
aerobic respiration 35-36
alkali metals 106-108
alleles 11-12
allotropes 90
alloys 105
anaerobic respiration 36
analysis 116-119
animal cells 19-20
arteries 57-58
asexual reproduction 14
atom economy 138
atomic number 70-71, 79
atomic spectroscopy 119
atomic structure 69-70, 210-212
atoms 69-77, 210-212
ATP 36

background radiation 216-217
bacteria 21
bases 9, 22-24
batch processes 97
blast furnace 109
blood 56-58, 62
Bohr, Neils 74
bond energy 147
buckminster fullerene 96

calorimetry 149-150
capillaries 63
carbon dating 222
carbonates 114
catalysts 24, 95, 109, 142,
    144, 148
cell division 26-29
cells 19-42
chain reactions 224
chemical formulae 76
chemical symbols 75
chromatography 97, 116-118
chromosomes 9-12, 22
circuit symbols 190
circuits 190-200
circulation 58
cloning 13-14
cold fusion 226

collisions 167-168
concentration 142
conductors 184-186, 192, 196
conservation of mass 81
contamination 218-219, 221
continuous processes 97
copper 109-110
covalent bonding 76, 84-87
covalent molecules 87-90
cracking 144
crop spraying 188
current 191-193

Dalton, John 73
defibrillators 189
deoxyribonucleic acid 9, 22-24, 27
diamond 89-90
differentiation 29-30
diffusion 32-33, 60
digestion 61-63
diodes 199-200
displacement reactions 94, 150
displacement–time graphs 158
distance 156-158
distance–time graphs 157-158
DNA 9, 22-24, 27
drag 164-165
drugs 97-98
dry mass 31

ecosystems 43-45
elasticity 164
electric charge 184-189, 191
electricity 184-204
electrolysis 110, 127-129
electrons 69-71, 76, 104-105, 196,
    210-211
electrostatic precipitators 187
elements 69, 78-80, 106
empirical formula 139
emulsifiers 62
endothermic reactions 143-144, 146
energy change 149-151
energy level diagrams 148
energy, conservation of 175
enzymes 24-26, 61-63
equations 77, 81-83, 94, 136, 211
equilibrium 145
ethanol 138-139
exothermic reactions 143-144, 146

fermentation 36
fertilisation 10
filament lamps 198
flame tests 112
food preservation 50-51
food production 49-50
forces 162-178
formulae 113-114
fractional distillation 144
friction 164-165, 169, 175-176
fuses 202-203

gametes 10, 29
gas tests 111
gauging 221
gene technology 13-16
genes 9-18
genetic disorders 12
genetic engineering 15
genetic modification 15
genetic screening 12
genetics 9-18
genotypes 11-12
GM crops 15-16
graphite 90
graphs 158–162
gravitational potential energy
    (GPE) 172-174
gravity 170, 172-173
group 1 106-108
group 7 91-94
groups 71, 74, 79
growth curves 30
growth 30-32

Haber process 109, 144-145
half-lives 215
halide ions 14
halogens 91-94
hazard symbols 112
heart 57-58
hydrosphere 129
hydroxide tests 115

insulators 184-186
intensive farming 49
interaction pairs 169
ionic bonding 76-77, 84-86, 88,
    113-114
ionic compounds 77, 113-114
ions 104, 114-115

Index

ions 74, 80, 84-86, 91, 123-124, 127-128, 196, 218
iron 109
irradiation 218-219, 221
isotopes 47, 71-72, 133, 219-220

kinetic energy 173-174, 177

light dependent resistor (LDRs) 199
light emitting diodes (LED) 199

mains electricity 201-204
mass 136-138, 162-163
mass number 70-71
mass spectroscopy 119
medical tracers 220
meiosis 27-28
Mendel, Gregor 11
Mendeleev, Dimitri 79
metabolism 35
metal carbonates 125-126
metal oxides 124
metallic structure 104
metals 104-110, 124-126
mitosis 27-28
moles 134-135
momentum 166-168, 170-171
multicellular organisms 20-21
mutation 10, 28-29, 218

nanoparticles 51, 95
nets 44
neutralisation reactions 123-124
Newlands' law of octaves 78
Newton's Laws 167
noble gases 79
nuclear fission 223-225
nuclear fusion 225-226
nuclear reactors 224

Ohm's Law 196
organic farming 50
organs 20
osmosis 33-34, 59-60
oxidation 108
oxygen debt 36

peer review 226
percentage yield 138
periodic table 71-74, 78-80
periods 71, 74

pH 123
phenotypes 11-12
phloem 59
photosynthesis 46-48
pitfall traps 44
plant cells 19-20
plant extracts 97-98
plasma 56
plasmolysis 34
pollution 130
pooters 44
potential difference 192-196
power 177, 203-204
precipitation reactions 83-84, 125
pressure 142, 144-145
protein synthesis 23-24
proteins 23-26

quadrats 44

radiation dose 219
radioactive decay 213-215
radioactive waste 225
radioactivity 210-226
reaction rates 139-142
recoil 171
reduction 93
relative atomic mass 133-135
relative formula mass 134-136
reproduction 10, 14
residual current circuit breakers (RCCB) 203
resistance 195-200, 204
resistors 196-200
respiration 35-37
respiratory quotient 37
resultant forces 163
reversible reactions 143-145
Rf values 117
RNA 23-24
Rutherford, Ernest 73

salts 124-126
sampling 43-45
seawater 127, 130
sex determination 10
sexual reproduction 10
smart alloys 105
smoke detectors 221
sodium chloride 127-129
solubility 130

spectator ions 84
spectroscopy 119
speed 156-160
speed–time graphs 160
spray painting 187
state symbols 82-83
steel 109
stem cells 14-15, 30
sterilisation 221
stopping distances 176
sulfate ions 114
superconductors 105-106
sustainability 99, 138
synthesis 96-99

terminal velocity 165
thermal decomposition 146
thermistors 199
tissues 20
tracers 221
transcription 23
transects 44
transition metals 78, 80, 109-110
translation 23
translocation 59
transpiration 59-60

variable resistors 199-200
variation 28-29
veins 57-58
velocity 156-157, 161
velocity–time graphs 161
voltage 192-196

water 129-130
weight 162-163, 170
work done 172-173

xylem 59

zonation 45

Periodic table

1	2											3	4	5	6	7	0
																	4 He helium 2
7 Li lithium 3	9 Be beryllium 4											11 B boron 5	12 C carbon 6	14 N nitrogen 7	16 O oxygen 8	19 F fluorine 9	20 Ne neon 10
23 Na sodium 11	24 Mg magnesium 12											27 Al aluminium 13	28 Si silicon 14	31 P phosphorus 15	32 S sulfur 16	35.5 Cl chlorine 17	40 Ar argon 18
39 K potassium 19	40 Ca calcium 20	45 Sc scandium 21	48 Ti titanium 22	51 V vanadium 23	52 Cr chromium 24	55 Mn manganese 25	56 Fe iron 26	59 Co cobalt 27	59 Ni nickel 28	63.5 Cu copper 29	65 Zn zinc 30	70 Ga gallium 31	73 Ge germanium 32	75 As arsenic 33	79 Se selenium 34	80 Br bromine 35	84 Kr krypton 36
85 Rb rubidium 37	88 Sr strontium 38	89 Y yttrium 39	91 Zr zirconium 40	93 Nb niobium 41	96 Mo molybdenum 42	[98] Tc technetium 43	101 Ru ruthenium 44	103 Rh rhodium 45	106 Pd palladium 46	108 Ag silver 47	112 Cd cadmium 48	115 In indium 49	119 Sn tin 50	122 Sb antimony 51	128 Te tellurium 52	127 I iodine 53	131 Xe xenon 54
133 Cs caesium 55	137 Ba barium 56	139 La* lanthanum 57	178 Hf hafnium 72	181 Ta tantalum 73	184 W tungsten 74	186 Re rhenium 75	190 Os osmium 76	192 Ir iridium 77	195 Pt platinum 78	197 Au gold 79	201 Hg mercury 80	204 Tl thallium 81	207 Pb lead 82	209 Bi bismuth 83	[209] Po polonium 84	[210] At astatine 85	[222] Rn radon 86
[223] Fr francium 87	[226] Ra radium 88	[227] Ac* actinium 89	[261] Rf rutherfordium 104	[262] Db dubnium 105	[266] Sg seaborgium 106	[264] Bh bohrium 107	[277] Hs hassium 108	[268] Mt meitnerium 109	[271] Ds darmstadtium 110	[272] Rg roentgenium 111							

Elements with atomic numbers 112–116 have been reported but not fully authenticated

*The Lanthanides (atomic numbers 58–71) and the Actinides (atomic numbers 90–103) have been omitted.

Cu and **Cl** have not been rounded to the nearest whole number.